FORESIGHT

A FUTURIST EXPLORES THE
TRENDS TRANSFORMING TOMORROW

JACK ULDRICH
WITH
SIMON ANDERSON

ISBN 13: 978-1-59298-894-5

Library of Congress Catalog Number: 2014922739
Printed in the United States of America
First Printing: 2012
Second Printing: 2012
Third Printing: 2013
Fourth Printing: 2015

19   18   17   16   15   8   7   6   5   4

Cover and interior designs by Lift Creative.

Beaver's Pond Press, Inc.
7108 Ohms Lane
Edina, MN 55439
(952) 829-8818
www.BeaversPondPress.com

To order, visit www.ItascaBooks.com or call 800-901-3480.
Reseller discounts available.

To my wife, Cindy, and my children, Meghan and Sean, who keep me grounded while I scan tomorrow's horizons.

JACK ULDRICH

To my parents, Donald and Susan Anderson, who encouraged my limitless curiosity as a child and whose confidence in me has still never wavered.

SIMON ANDERSON

CONTENTS

INTRODUCTION

The year 2020: it has a futuristic ring, doesn't it? To some people, it might seem distant; and, in an era of accelerating change, it is far away in the sense that emerging technologies will create new businesses and business models—as well as deconstruct existing ones—at an ever-faster rate between now and the year 2020.

It is often said that hindsight is 20/20, but looking back just ten years to 2004, who could have foreseen Facebook exploding to over one billion members and, in the process, changing the nature of how society communicates? Who could have predicted that a collaborative effort between millions of unpaid individuals would lead to the creation of Wikipedia—the world's most comprehensive and accessible encyclopedia? Who could have guessed that Twitter, an eight-year-old micro-blogging service, would play a significant role in overthrowing longstanding authoritarian regimes in the Middle East, or that YouTube viewers would seize the platform to create and upload 100 hours of video to YouTube every minute, or that AirBnB would facilitate the rental of 20,000 rooms in Paris in a single evening or that Uber would threaten the entire taxi service business model and have an estimated value of more than $18 billion? And, who would have speculated that Apple, with its introduction of the iPhone (and its millions of apps) in 2007 and the iPad in 2009, would become one of the world's largest corporations, or that the Amazon Kindle (introduced in 2008) would make it more probable that you are reading this as an ebook than a paper book?

It is both exciting and daunting to consider what the rest of this decade could hold. Yet, if perfect hindsight still leaves our heads and minds spinning at the scale and magnitude of past change, is it the ultimate hubris to think that anyone can accurately predict the future?

To be honest, yes.

Each year information technology is only getting better, faster, and cheaper, and hundreds of millions of new individuals are being drawn into a hyper-connected and networked global economy. The previously unknown ideas and insights of those hundreds of millions of individuals are now being added to the global consciousness, further accelerating change.

This book, then, is not intended to be consumed with a rigid or dogmatic belief that each scenario and forecast offers a literal prediction of what the future holds. Although written in a descriptive style, the scenarios are designed to introduce the reader to the major trends shaping the world of tomorrow, while at the same time providing insights into how the future might unfold.

Foresight 20/20 is meant to be read with a discerning eye, and you are encouraged to challenge the details about what is presented in this book. As the authors, we concede our vision—like everyone else's—may be clouded by past history as well as faulty assumptions, beliefs, and biases of which we are not even aware. We also humbly acknowledge that, while we both work as professional futurists and forecasters, there will always be more that we don't know than what we do know.

What then is the purpose of the book?

It is designed to help you create the future by thinking about it in a new light. To do this, we begin with a chapter on an area that is frequently overlooked by futurists, yet always influences the future in profoundly powerful ways: unexpected (and often catastrophic) events.

As one wise forecaster once said, "The only thing I'm certain of is that there is too much certainty in this world." Few experts are willing to acknowledge what they don't know, but in this chapter we strive to offer a list of possible events that could cause the future to swerve in some unexpected directions. By their very nature, however, these unknown or "Black Swan"—low probability, but high impact—events are, well, unknown.

Still, it behooves anyone interested in preparing for the future to contemplate how large, random events—be it in the form of a cyber-terrorism attack, a massive solar storm or volcanic eruption, a global pandemic, or any number of other man-made or natural disasters—might alter the arc of future trends.

The reason is twofold. First, "thinking about the unthinkable" is an excellent way to remind oneself to always "expect the unexpected." This, in turn, reminds individuals and organizations to focus on integrating the principles of flexibility and adaptability into their strategic planning processes. In the future, "change will be the only constant," and it's imperative to always keep this idea top of mind.

In spite of such large-scale unexpected events (as are outlined in the opening chapter), the future will still move forward just as the massive shocks to the world in the last century—the

First World War, the great influenza outbreak of 1918, the Great Depression, and the Second World War, etc.—did little to slow the twentieth century's relentless march toward industrialization and globalization.

The same will be true in the coming decade, and it is the broad nature of technological change that this book will be primarily centered upon. Chapter Two delves into how the extraordinary changes in wearable technology, "Big Data" and biotechnology are creating a world of highly individualized, preventative health care and how this will change the face of modern medicine. Chapter Three looks at advancements in the world of manufacturing, but concentrates on how accelerating advances in 3D manufacturing are making physical materials almost as easy to manipulate as data. Chapter Four reviews how the world of education will be transformed by technology, and addresses the implications for students, educators, and administrators. Chapter Five offers a glimpse into the future of transportation and Chapter Six into how technological changes and human behavior will be altered as agribusinesses, farmers, and citizens struggle to successfully feed the half-billion new people who will occupy the planet by the end of the decade. Chapter Seven concerns itself with how the production of energy (specifically electricity) is becoming more decentralized, cleaner, and easier for the average consumer to control. Chapter Eight provides an overview of the ways retailers and consumers will adjust and modify their behavior in response to ubiquitous information and connectedness. Chapter Nine looks into the future of law enforcement, and Chapter Ten the future of banking and finance. The final three chapters are broader in scope and discuss how the three megatrends of robotics, artificial intelligence, and gaming dynamics will invade people's everyday lives.

Each chapter is written as a narrative in order to make the

changes more relatable, and it is our expectation that after reading this book you will be able to better position yourself and your organization to take advantage of the future's nearly unlimited possibilities.

We encourage you to be an active participant while reading this book, and discuss the scenarios and ideas with your colleagues and team members. Feel free to ask tough and critical questions: What did we get wrong? What technologies did we miss? What other factors (i.e. political, regulatory, legal, etc.) might slow down or speed up certain technologies? How might consumers and competitors react differently than we predict?

And how might some technologies converge with others and spin off in unexpected directions? The ability to foresee and adapt to emerging technologies and trends is necessary for the ongoing success of any business, and we hope that we have created a catalyst for you to begin considering the future when planning today.

This last step is particularly critical because, as business forecasters, the one thing we know for certain is that it will be individuals like you who will create the future, and armed with "Foresight 20/20", we are confident you can and will create a future that is bigger, bolder, and better than the one presented in this book.

Jack Uldrich and Simon Anderson
January 2015

1

FUTURE FORECAST: HAZY WITH A CHANCE OF CATASTROPHE

At 2:46 p.m. on Friday, March 11, 2011, a magnitude 9.0 earthquake struck Japan. Less than seven minutes later a massive tsunami traveling 500 miles per hour slammed into the northeast coast of the island nation, destroying hundreds of thousands of homes and buildings. It left little in the area untouched, including one of the world's largest nuclear facilities—the Fukushima Daiichi nuclear complex. The partial meltdown of four of the facility's six reactors reignited serious debate regarding the long-term viability and safety of nuclear power. In addition to affecting the continued expansion of nuclear power, the event could prove to be a boon to the future development of cleaner, safer, and more distributed forms of energy such as fuel cell, solar, or even wave/tidal power.

A few countries also responded to the meltdown by announcing the end of operations at their existing nuclear power facilities and forcing them to revert back to older methods of power generation, such as burning coal or natural gas. This is due to the fact that many newer methods of generating electricity lack the ability to scale quickly enough to replace the power lost from shuttering nuclear plants.

The Japanese earthquake/tsunami disaster serves as a poignant reminder that forecasting trends is a complex task because, so often, unexpected and unforeseen events have a way of altering how trends unfold in the future. Consider, for example, how the events of 9/11 (and the subsequent wars in Iraq and Afghanistan) spurred the development of robots and unmanned aerial vehicles, or how the 2008 subprime mortgage fiasco caused the capital markets to dry up for eighteen months and lead to the enactment of many new restrictive financial regulations on banks and financial institutions.

To illustrate how a series of similar low-probability but high-impact events might shape the world of 2020 in some unexpected ways, let's observe A Decade of Disasters, a retrospective of the past decade (2010–2019) produced by the BBC's Global Crowdsource Network and released on December 31, 2019. The report began with an overview of the 2010 BP "Deep Horizon" oil spill and showed how it temporarily slowed the progression of offshore drilling operations in the United States. The report then moved on to the Japanese earthquake and tsunami of 2011, and discussed how it spurred the creation of radical new building and architectural designs. It went on to present the widespread destruction that Hurricane Sandy leveled on the Northeast coast of the United States in late fall of 2012, and was followed by a brief review of how the massive train derailments in Quebec and Spain in the summer of 2013 and the disappearance of Malaysian Airline Flight 370 spurred major changes in the rail and airline industries.

Below is an abbreviated synopsis of the report beginning with the year 2015:

In August of that year, a freakishly large solar storm—classified as a once-in-one-hundred-year event—disrupted a number of global telecommunications satellites. In the ensuing blackout, a commercial iridium satellite collided with a defunct Russian satellite. The cloud of wreckage created thousands of new pieces of space debris that, in turn, knocked out three more critical communications satellites. For the better part of a week, vital military, financial, business, and logistics facilities had little to no access to satellite service as hundreds of the satellites were repositioned to avoid the new debris and further damage.

In addition to disrupting the global supply chain and depressing the retail industry's sales and revenues expectations for the 2015 Christmas holiday season, the incident revealed the vulnerability of the global satellite network and highlighted the growing problem of space debris. The event lead to increased investment in the development of new "nanosatellites" and renewed interest in the private sector in creating various lower atmosphere communications platforms including high flying solar planes that provided more localized coverage.

In January 2016, using lessons learned from the hacking of an American surveillance drone a few years earlier, operatives of an organization covertly funded by the Iranian army electronically hijacked an American unmanned aerial vehicle (UAV) and fired its missiles at an Israeli settlement on the West Bank. Seventeen civilians, including ten school-aged children, were killed. The attack triggered a new round of tension in the Middle East and sent gas prices soaring toward $6 a gallon for the first time in American history. In response to the pain consumers were feeling at the gas pump, Congress approved a $3 billion battery advancement program, and ten companies received grants in excess of $150 million to improve the capacity and charging times of power storage units in electric vehicles.

In a related development, a number of international organizations called for a review of the role of robotic devices in warfare. No discernible course of action was agreed upon but the stock price of a number of leading robotics firms suffered declines of up to 60 percent, and the production of next-generation military robots was delayed as a result. Later that year, thousands of previously classified diplomatic files were released by OpenLeaks, a group operating in the tradition of WikiLeaks. Among the disclosures was a video clip showing members of a Middle Eastern royal family engaging in sexual relations with Western prostitutes in London. The disclosure triggered a violent public uprising. Adding to ongoing and increasingly violent protests and unrest already present in the region, the resulting upheaval was brutally put down by the government and pushed oil prices above $200 a barrel; gas prices in the U.S. spiked to $7.50 per gallon. This event, along with new advancements in battery technology and graphene, was later credited with being the impetus that finally caused American consumers to embrace hybrid and all-electric vehicles on a wide scale. The number of companies working to develop better batteries increased ten-fold by the end of 2016 driving the cost per kwH down dramatically.

The oil shock caused the Canadian government to hastily approve the construction of additional pipelines to carry oil from mining operations in the Alberta oil sands and offered generous incentives to companies capable of building them quickly. Environmentalists' concerns over greenhouse gas emissions and polluted water went unheeded over the chorus of consumers clamoring for the government to "do something" about high energy prices. In a related development, the US Congress approved a $10 billion initiative to pursue advances in synthetic biology in hopes that a breakthrough in the field could reduce the nation's reliance on oil. (Four years later, Exxon Mobil opened the first large-scale synthetic biology oil production facility in southern Arizona.)

On the Friday before Memorial Day in 2016, the world's financial markets were shocked when a group of hackers located on the outskirts of Moscow infiltrated the computer systems of both the Euronext Paris (the French stock market) and EDF, France's largest public utility. The latter attack plunged seventeen million French citizens into darkness for an entire weekend and spurred the European Union to establish a 50 percent mandate for the production of distributed forms of energy by 2030.

The attack on the French market caused an estimated $250 billion in market capital to be wiped out as skittish investors pulled their money out of the market. These events, in combination with a series of other lower-level and less-damaging attacks against one of the world's largest insurance company's cloud databases earlier in the year, further heightened concern over government-sponsored hackers and independent cybercriminals' ability to penetrate systems previously believed to be invulnerable to them. It also dealt a serious blow to the cloud computing industry as companies raced to revisit their approach to information management in wake of the high-profile attacks.

Across the Atlantic in the fall of 2016, a prestigious medical journal released a study linking the spread of carbon nanotubes—which were small enough to penetrate the blood-brain barrier—with slower-than-normal mental development of children under the age of five. Although the study was later found to be flawed, the damage to companies using carbon nanotubes and nanoparticles was significant because numerous states rushed to pass laws severely restricting how the materials could be used. Among the industries hardest hit was the pharmaceutical industry.

In January 2017, the most serious pandemic in a century began in the small rural city of La Barca, Mexico. From there, the infection spread undetected to Mexico City. Due to the Mexican government's unwillingness to impose quarantine on international travelers for fear of what it would do to the country's tourism industry, which was already in serious decline due to drug cartel violence, hundreds of infected business travelers carried the disease back to their home countries. The speed and the deadly nature of the pandemic stunned the Center for Disease Control and the World Health Organization, and by June an estimated 1.5 million people—primarily children and the elderly—had died.

Although new, more efficient processes were now being used to replace the old method of using fertilized chicken eggs to produce vaccines, global demand for the hastily produced vaccination soon overwhelmed the pharmaceutical industry's limited capability. This sparked an uproar in the developing nations, as upper-middle class residents in the developed nations received the majority of what was produced. The ensuing crisis brought to light long-festering problems in the United Nations and further eroded the effectiveness of that international governing body. The pandemic once again highlighted how corporations, industries, and governments in their never-ending quest for efficiency had created a "just-in-time" global supply chain that valued short-term efficiency over long-term endurance. The vulnerability of this strategy was quickly exposed as critical shipping, air, rail, and transport logistics facilities were shut down for weeks on end when employees refused to report for work. Additionally, many corporations simply refused to produce the vaccine as its price was set by a well-intentioned, but ultimately counterproductive, international regulatory agency to a level that was not profitable enough for them to justify the necessary infrastructure or distribution changes. As a result, a number of life-sustaining drugs could not be delivered to hospitals and pharmacies—even in areas not directly affected by the pandemic. It was later estimated the breakdown in the global supply chain resulted in an additional 400,000 deaths—mostly in the first world. The deaths did not go unnoticed and were credited with spurring a renewed worldwide interest in supplementary "just-in-case" supply chain management. The pandemic was also credited with sparking the creation of numerous rapid diagnostic technologies. (Consequently, many governments raced to repeal laws restricting the use of carbon nanotubes and nanoparticles because many of the best diagnostic tools had been inadvertently banned under the legislation.)

In July 2018, just as the global economy was recovering from the "Great Pandemic of 2017," Mount Merapi, a volcano in Indonesia erupted and spewed an estimated fifteen billion metric tons of ash into the atmosphere. The ash reflected so much sunlight back into the outer atmosphere that scientists later calculated the overall temperature on Earth in 2018 fell a full degree Fahrenheit. The temperature differential, while seemingly small, temporarily reversed a long trend of global warming and the sudden change was enough to cause severe drought conditions in Europe, Russia, Australia, and Argentina. Global production of wheat plummeted 23 percent, creating major food shortages around the world. In response, European governments, desperate to feed their populations, agreed to remove their decades-long prohibition against genetically modified crops by allowing some newer enhanced crops to be planted. (Interestingly, the countries made these concessions in spite of strong scientific evidence suggesting a growing number of insects were becoming resistant to a growing number of genetically modified crops.) The action was not enough, however, to prevent a series of intense riots in Moscow, Paris, Brussels, and Rome over the critical shortage of food. Shortly thereafter, progressive governments in Italy, France, and the United Kingdom—which had only a year earlier ridden to power in the wake of their predecessor's inability to meet the threats of the global pandemic—fell to their more conservative counterparts.

The combined effects of the pandemic and volcanic eruption spilled over into 2019 as food scarcity and uneven distribution led to unrest in China. The large number of new nanosatellites created in the wake of the 2015 "space disaster" made it difficult for the ruling party to control communications and, fearing an overthrow of its government, Chinese government officials launched a fierce crackdown on its own citizens. As a diversion, the state also began making boisterous claims against the government of Taiwan, which it said was inciting the opposition. As the situation between the two Asian adversaries grew tenser, the United States sent three carrier battle groups into the Sea of Taiwan. The talk of a "Cold War II"—this time between the US and China—played directly into the hands of the Republican Party and it was able to parlay its platform of "strong national defense" into a solid majority in the House and Senate. The first act of the new Congress of 2019 was to pass the largest defense budget in U.S. history. China responded in kind and also reasserted its intended goal of dominating outer space.

No sooner had Congress approved the 2019 defense budget than a small but well-trained group of ecoterrorists—claiming the Brazilian government was irrevocably destroying the Amazon Basin—released a deadly nerve agent in the administrative offices of the Brazilian parliament, killing 160 people. It was the first large-scale bioterrorist attack, and its impact reverberated around the globe as scores of governments began investing in various bioterrorism defenses as well as cracking down on the civil liberties of dissidents and opposition groups.

The program, A Decade of Disasters, concluded with the host saying, "If the past decade has taught us anything, it is that we must expect the unexpected." She then closed by reporting on two recent stories. One discussed how experimental samples at Exxon Mobil's synthetic biology oil facility in Arizona were found to be responsible for contaminating agricultural crops in Mexico. The finding, which was disputed by Exxon officials, deepened the rift originally created between the governments of Mexico and the United States in the aftermath of the pandemic of 2017. The second item reported how groundwater polluted by the oil sands was leeching into U.S. rivers and affecting drinking water from Minnesota to Louisiana. Not only was the problem causing a strain in U.S.–Canadian relations, a new scientific study had just been released linking the contaminated water with an abnormally high number of children born with genetic defects along the affected waterways. The host concluded the program by saying, "The world continues to grow smaller and more interconnected, and the pace of technological change is accelerating. The forecast for the future remains hazy with a chance of catastrophe."

— BONUS QUESTIONS —

How has an unexpected natural disaster affected your life or your business?

What natural disasters are more likely to occur in your area? What are types of disasters that, while unlikely to occur where you live, could still cause major damage?

Are you properly prepared for disaster? (Insurance, manufacturing contingency, etc.)

Identify at least one rare or unlikely event which, if it were to occur, would be a "game changer" for your company or industry.

Is it reasonable to expect that another major disaster (natural or otherwise) will strike the United States in the next decade? What about in the next year?

Will science ever make it possible to predict tsunamis, earthquakes, volcanic eruptions, or other natural disasters days (or even weeks) in advance? How will this affect our lives and businesses?

Who in your organization is responsible for "thinking about the unthinkable" and "expecting the unexpected?"

2

THE HEART OF THE MATTER: THE FUTURE OF HEALTH CARE

In January of 2014, Illumina, a San Diego based company, announced that their high throughput genetic sequencing machine "HiSeq X Ten" had finally broken through the long sought after $1,000 barrier to sequence a full human genome and could sequence up to five per day. To put this in some perspective, it helps to consider that the first human genome project was completed in 2001 for the sum of three billion dollars. The project has already had major implications for the health care industry and the way we prevent and treat disease. Alas, fast and inexpensive gene sequencing is just a small part of the incredible changes already occurring in the field of health care.

By the beginning of the next decade, in addition to the developments in genomics, genomic surgery, continued advances in information technology, biotechnology, nanotechnology, robotics, data mining, wearable technologies, artificial intelligence, sensors, social networking, and myriad other technologies will transform the face of modern medicine. What follows is a scenario involving one individual with a single ailment.

FUTURE SCENARIO

On October 21, 2020, Roger Martin, a sixty-seven-year-old, under-employed attorney, suffered a massive heart attack while tending to a small plot of land on an urban farm in a once thriving suburb of Atlanta. Had the event occurred ten years earlier, Roger, an early adopter of the "P4" (predictive, preventive, personalized, and participatory) mobile medicine, would not have made it to the hospital alive.

The first sign of impending danger came when sensors in Roger's shirt detected an unusually high pulse. Unbeknownst to Roger, his shirt sent a wireless alert to his "PMD" (personal mobile device) so it could begin to more closely monitor his other vital signs. After noting his symptoms, it compared them, along with his medical history and genetic file, to its vast database of all known diseases and injuries. Among the possible causes were a number of serious conditions, so it also contacted his primary physician, who immediately contacted Roger via mobile video connection.

"How are you feeling, Roger?"

"Fine," he replied, "maybe a little tired, but nothing out of the ordinary."

Seeing that Roger looked a little pale, the doctor asked him if he had his permission to activate a mesh network of nanoscale diagnostic chips that had been placed inside Roger's body following his first heart attack in 2017.

"What if it's another false alarm?" asked Roger, who had been contacted by his doctor in response to a similar situation last year.

"I'm not 100 percent sure it isn't," replied his doctor. "The technology's still far from perfect, but I don't want to take a chance. Do you?"

"No, but are you sure the signals from those little nanobots won't do more harm than good?" asked Roger, who was still nervous about the chips' efficacy after hearing various reports from some news organizations hinting at the possibility that activated chips could be contributing to the recent rise in reported cancer cases.

"The rise in rates has nothing to do with the chips themselves," said the doctor, "and everything to do with our ability to detect cancer at an earlier stage. If you need further evidence," continued the doctor, "I suggest you query your personal assistant on your PMD. It'll confirm your worries are based on nothing more than an insidious urban myth. I can't believe it still persists in this day and age."

After gaining Roger's approval, moments later, the network of nanometer-sized circuits patrolling Roger's arteries was activated and began sampling his blood. Within seconds, the doctor was made aware that the level of C-reactive proteins in Roger's blood was abnormally high.

The doctor's voice took on a more serious tone. "Roger, I want you to sit down, stop whatever you're doing and take a deep breath." Roger did as instructed.

"Now, I want you to remain calm—and please know that I'm going to be with you the entire time—but there's a good chance you're on the verge of having a serious heart attack. The nearest hospital has been alerted, and an ambulance is already on its way."

"You're kidding, right? I'm just feeling a little tired. All I've been doing is working outside—getting some fresh air and exercise like you suggested."

"Just relax, Roger. Over the last few years, I've come to appreciate the system's ability to more quickly and accurately diagnose health-care-related issues than either I—or my patients—can. Plus, better to be safe than sorry, right?"

"Yeah, I guess," replied Roger pensively as his breath became more labored. In an attempt to lighten the mood, he added, "I hate to think what this will do to my insurance rates."

By the time the ambulance had arrived, Roger was thankful to see it because he had begun to feel constricted in his chest. Then, only moments after being placed in the ambulance, Roger went into full cardiac arrest. The paramedics were prepared and followed the new protocol established by the American Medical Association in 2018. Normally, Roger would have been taken to Emory University hospital, but due to traffic congestion and the severity of his condition, the ambulance was rerouted by an intelligent traffic system to an outpatient clinic located just off the freeway. Once there, Roger was whisked away on a gurney to a "clean" room where he was anesthetized and prepped for surgery. Then, in a procedure that would have been all but unthinkable even five years earlier and which was approved just the previous year by the Food and Drug Administration for emergency situations, a robotic surgical device was wheeled into the room and positioned over Roger. With only a nurse and a young attending doctor in the room, a heart specialist located in Havana—connected via a secure, redundant fiber optic Internet connection—began guiding the thin, flexible arms of the device through the intricate surgical procedure using nothing but hand-gestures.

When the surgery was completed just twenty-three minutes later, all that was visible on Roger's chest was a Band-Aid-sized incision where the robotic arm had entered his chest cavity to insert a temporary stent.

Roger awoke a little later and was greeted by a split screen display showing the heart surgeon and his primary physician. "You're lucky to be alive," said his doctor. "I'd now like to introduce you to the person responsible for extending your life, Dr. Daniela Famosa. Under the recently passed International Health Services Act, she was able to perform your surgery from Cuba."

Roger smiled and nodded in her direction.

"During the operation," said Dr. Famosa, "I harvested some of your stem cells and, with your permission, I'd like to have them transferred to the Institute for Regenerative Medicine at Wake Forest University where they will grow you a new, fully compatible artery. If all goes according to plan it should be ready in two weeks and can be inserted the week before Thanksgiving. Based on your personal health record and history of patients with a similar health background to you, you should even be able to travel over the holidays if you want."

"You'll have to stay away from the eggnog this year," she added with a wink.

Later that afternoon, Roger was discussing his outpatient treatment with "Cindy"—a computer animated avatar program on his PMD that acted as his personal nurse. The avatar, which Roger liked to call his "cyber twin sister," was responsible for continuously monitoring his health status in addition to scanning the latest health care information in order to recommend and deliver Roger the best possible care.

"Based on your genetic profile and the presence of the following genes—SMAD3 and CXCL 12," said Cindy in a soothing and reassuring voice, "we know that the blood thinner warfarin—Type C3—will work best for you during this interim period. It's also recommended that you not take it with any of the other following drugs." His cyber twin went to list those drugs that Roger was to avoid, including the new antidepressant he had been prescribed. (In early 2020, the FDA was forced to pull the leading electronic brain stimulant treatment for depression after numerous patients in the first test group began losing feeling in their legs and feet.)

"I realize this is a lot of information for you to process right now. Don't worry," continued Cindy, "I'll remind you when to take your medication." In a tone that then offered just the slightest hint of admonition, the avatar added, "When your heart is ready, we'll also do a better job of keeping you on track with your exercise regimen." Roger voiced his approval.

"Are there other questions I can answer for you?" queried Cindy.

"Well," said Roger, who, in spite of avatars' growing popularity the past few years, was still a little surprised with how natural it felt to be conversing with a virtual nurse, "could you tell me a little more about how the doctors are going to grow my new artery and install it?"

"Sure." Cindy promptly called forth the 3D digital scans of Roger's heart and showed him the blocked artery that had been color-highlighted for his convenience. The avatar went on to explain how plaque, fatty substances, cholesterol, cellular waste, and calcium had been slowly building up over time and this combination was the main culprit of his heart attack. The avatar then suggested viewing a simulation with his virtual reality goggles.

"I thought that contraption was only good for playing games with my grandson," replied Roger with a laugh.

Once Cindy recognized that Roger understood the cause of his heart attack—which she determined by using facial recognition technology to scan his physical reaction to the information that was being presented—she went on to show him how his new artery would be grown. Cindy called up a short video tutorial produced by the Institute of Regenerative Medicine demonstrating how a small scaffold would first be constructed using biocompatible material and a 3D printer, and how that scaffold was then seeded with Roger's own stem cells and cultured until an artery replacement of precise proportions was grown. "There's virtually no chance your body will reject the new part," said Cindy. The avatar explained other treatment options to Roger along with the costs and benefits of each procedure. "I'm happy to arrange a conversation with a doctor if you have any additional questions, but I recommend the replacement surgery."

Roger asked Cindy a few questions regarding his insurance coverage and what costs he would be responsible for, but once satisfied with those answers Roger indicated he didn't have any additional questions. The avatar then began preparing him for outpatient services.

"The first thing we'll need to do is outfit you with a new line of sensor-embedded clothing. Your current wearable bands are pretty good in terms of monitoring your vital signs, but as an extra precaution we'll want to keep extra close tabs on you during your recovery period."

Continuing, Cindy said, "I have also taken the liberty of putting together a list of friends and colleagues who have either had heart attacks or have lived with someone who has had one."

Knowing that Roger was the type of person who responded better to scientific information, Cindy added, "Past heart attack patients who have joined health networks are 37 percent less likely to suffer a repeat heart attack within the next five years. They also experience an increase in life expectancy of 2.8 years over those who don't."

To make the point more vivid, Cindy displayed the information using a visually compelling chart on one of the nearby screens. She added, "A good way to use your network is to enroll in Healthy Hearts, your insurance provider's new game to encourage an active and healthy lifestyle. It's possible your rates could go down in the future if you score above the eighty-fifth percentile."

Two months after his successful artery replacement surgery, Roger received a small scale 3D model of a human heart when he refilled his personally tailored heart medication prescription. It was a discount offer from a new biotech company that had only recently begun growing and marketing human hearts. Roger activated the computer chip inside the model, which then displayed a holographic advertisement on this PMD. The ad read: "It's not too soon to begin thinking about your next heart. You can never know when you'll need it, but it sure 'beats' the alternative."

Roger then called up Cindy and asked her what the odds were that he would need a new heart by the year 2030.

"If you continue to follow the recommended therapy and exercise, 42 percent," replied Cindy. "Just as an FYI, due to your projected increase in life expectancy, the odds of you contracting prostate cancer have also increased. But don't worry, I'll keep a close eye on all the indicators and notify you if any action is necessary."

"Thanks." Roger turned back to his PMD and directed his personal assistant to revise his monthly budget so that he could afford his new heart when the time came as well as live comfortably for the few additional years that had just been added to his life.

— BONUS QUESTIONS —

Right now, it's highly unlikely that you have had your personal genome sequenced. What do you think the chance will be that you've had it sequenced by 2020?

Do you wear a personal monitoring device such as a FitBit or a Jawbone Up?

How do you feel about health care apps, such as those powered by IBM's Watson, providing your initial diagnosis?

Right now, robotic assistants, such as the Da Vinci machine, are helping surgeons perform complicated surgeries on their patients. How would you feel if the robot performed the surgery all by itself?

Do you think we will ever cure cancer, or will it continue to adapt to our advancements?

If genomic surgery could be performed on an embryo to prevent a genetic disease would you select that option? Do you believe insurance companies should be required to pay for such a surgery?

How do you feel about having a set of "backup" organs grown from small samples of your cells and stored in case you ever need them?

When planning for or thinking about retirement, what age are you expecting to live to? Given the rapid pace of advancement in medical technology, do you think that your expected longevity could change and require a new retirement plan?

3

SHAPING THINGS TO COME: THE FUTURE OF MANUFACTURING

In a nondescript lab in the mechanical engineering department at the University of Bath in England sits a machine as revolutionary as Gutenberg's printing press. The device, dubbed RepRap, is a rapid prototype manufacturer—a 3D printer—that can print physical objects. What makes RepRap so unusual and potentially transformative is that it can print many of its own components and it's completely open source, which allows anyone around the world to customize and improve its components. And while RepRap cannot yet print every part of itself, it is not difficult to imagine a day in the not-too-distant future when it will be able to achieve such an extraordinary feat.

The field of 3D manufacturing is quickly advancing. By the end of 2014, M3D LLC is promising to deliver a 3D printer to its Kickstarter contributors for $299 and by the end of the decade, 3D manufacturing could transform the manufacturing sector and the larger global economy in some surprising and unexpected ways. To better grasp the potential of this technology, let's observe a day in the life of Kim, a young Canadian artisan living in Toronto.

FUTURE SCENARIO

During her morning jog along the Humber River, Kim notices an interesting flower growing around a small tree, and it
inspires her to add a new necklace design to her growing line of
customized jewelry. Using her smartwatch, she takes a 3D photo of the flower to capture the details for later. When she gets
back to her apartment studio, Kim (who taught herself jewelry
design by taking a customized combination of courses that were
generated for her based on her interests, experience, and career
goals by the popular "College-at-Home" adaptive learning platform) sketches the design freehand in her notebook. She felt a
bit dated doing so, but she still preferred creating her first drafts
using a pencil to draw in an old notebook. After making a few
tweaks, she unfolds her flexible computer tablet and scans the
design into a sophisticated software program that suggests a few
modifications and renders the drawing into a three-dimensional
model. From her computer, Kim then views the drawing using
her virtual reality glasses and rotates it with a haptic glove so she
can view it from all angles. Kim accepts all of the computer's suggested changes and adds a few of her own in an effort to further
enhance the design.

The task of physically printing the first draft of the necklace
takes only a few minutes in spite of the fact that it incorporates
a series of small interlocking pieces that appear to have been assembled by hand, but were actually simultaneously printed. Such
a complicated design would have been impossible to produce
without an expensive commercial printer even a few years earlier.

Kim regularly meets with other "fabbers" in Toronto to share,
discuss and "hack" designs. Some of her colleagues are design-
ing and printing unique musical instruments, while innovative
engineers are using the technology to design new motors that
require no lubricants and will be more reliable, because they can

be printed already fully assembled to exacting specifications. Still others are experimenting with printing more complex electronics and batteries using graphene as well as innovative extrusion printers capable of creating designs with a 360-degree arc. As one fellow "fabber" said recently, "This technology is like having a factory at your house!" There is one thing that they all agree on: 3D manufacturing is allowing artisans and engineers to bypass old "form versus function" constraints and bring to life previously impossible designs.

After physically inspecting the initial prototype, Kim returns to her computer and makes a few modifications. Satisfied, she thought about uploading the design into the same ninety-nine-dollar printer she used to create the first version, however Kim opts to employ her new top-of-the-line 3D printer, because it can utilize cartridges of titanium—her material of choice for this particular necklace. Kim then hits a button and the 3D printer in her living room whirrs into action and, layer by layer, manufactures her necklace. By midafternoon, the jewelry is complete. Even though she has done this many times lately, Kim still shakes her head in wonder. Only hours earlier, the necklace had been nothing but an idea in her head and now she was holding the physical manifestation of her vision.

In past years, Kim would have uploaded the design directly to her website—where it could be interactively rotated for the viewing pleasure of admirers and potential buyers—and begun selling the final product. Unfortunately, recently 3D "pirates" had taken to stealing her and countless other people's original designs and selling the pirated work at a substantial discount. In an effort to combat the problem, Kim took the precautionary measure of creating and printing her designs with a unique mix of printable electronic coding tags and nanomaterials—both of which served to authenticate her work. These additions allowed Kim to continue to market and sell her work to high-end customers, although she knew a great many people couldn't differentiate between an original and a counterfeit piece of her work. Indeed, unless she looked closely for her specific nanomaterial tags, even she had a problem spotting the differences.

As someone who grew up listening to pirated music, Kim realizes counterfeiting is just the way of the world now. So, when she reflects on all the ways 3D manufacturing has improved her life, she has a hard time getting too upset about one of her occasional designs being boot-legged. Only the day before, Kim learned she needed to have a crown on a molar replaced. The entire process, which only a few years earlier would have cost $800 and required a return trip, was finished in less than thirty minutes and at a fraction of the previous cost. This was because the dentist could simply scan her tooth and print a perfect fitting replacement. In recent weeks, Kim has also printed a pair of designer shoes for herself as well as a customized action figure of Canada's most recent gold medal Olympic figure-skating champion for her seven-year-old niece.

The same technology has also allowed Kim to keep her 1964 Ford Mustang running smoothly for years. For instance, when her engine blew a gasket, she was able to download the design for the part and print it out in less than fifteen minutes. Kim remembers the old days when finding any spare part for her vintage automobile would have set off a time-consuming search for a supplier who still manufactured the part. Moreover, it would have cost a great deal of money and taken days to receive the part. Now she just visits the "Classics" section of Ford's website and downloads almost any part on her car for a fraction of the cost. The savings alone have justified her purchase of a 3D printer.

The real reason Kim is so pleased with additive manufacturing, however, is because of what it has meant for her loved ones. Her boyfriend, a Canadian Special Operations soldier, is alive today because of 3D printing. A search-and-destroy robot he was using to defuse bombs in eastern Africa was debilitated by a fast-exploding incendiary device, and his unit was able to swiftly get the robot operational again using a portable 3D printer that manufactured all of the damaged components on location. Later that day, the robot successfully detected a cleverly hidden roadside bomb which would have likely killed or severely injured him and other members of his unit.

Similar 3D printing technology has also dramatically improved the life of Kim's mother. After using her smart device to detect melanoma, a surgeon was able to remove the cancerous lesion and replace it with a swath of biocompatible skin that was printed out using her mother's own stem cells. The only way the new printable skin could be distinguished from the surrounding skin was that it looked slightly smoother and younger.

Kim is hopeful that just as 3D printing can keep her 1964 Mustang running for the foreseeable future, the technology will soon be able to do the same for her mom—who was born in 1944—by printing other body replacement parts, including kidneys, liver, lungs and, eventually, even a functioning heart.

However, when it comes to human organs being printed as easily as car parts, Kim is much less optimistic. Recently, members of the Conservative Party in Canada have introduced legislation seeking to severely limit the uses of 3D printing technology. While concerns over the technology's impact on the longevity of its citizens is an issue (experts estimate that the technology could increase average life expectancy five to ten years for patients who had access to it), the more pressing concern is what 3D printing technology has done to the Canadian manufacturing and transportation shipping sectors. (Before 3D printing's rapid rise, more than 1.5 million Canadians were employed in traditional manufacturing and supply chain distribution jobs, but that number has since plummeted.)

Kim and many of her peers in this emerging class of new entrepreneurs (who are now profitably employed by utilizing 3D printing technology) have countered that the technology is also creating new jobs, but the labor unions representing the traditional tool-and-die workers and delivery drivers who have lost their jobs—and who now have time to protest—have waged a successful public relations battle and appear to be swaying public opinion in their favor. Additionally, many business associations throughout Canada have recently begun to weigh in on the issue. The counterfeit reproductions of their member's products are of such high quality that many customers are now purchasing the lower cost forgeries and hampering sales of the genuine articles. Police and law enforcement groups have also joined in to oppose the technology on the grounds that criminal groups are now utilizing the technology to print high-quality handguns and assault rifles.

Kim shares the police's concern (but has printed her own handgun) and understands the frustration of the traditional manufacturers and shippers, but she believes these workers are modern-day Don Quixote's tilting against windmills. Kim can't imagine Canada or any other country in the world returning to yesteryear's outdated and inefficient manufacturing methods and models.

"Why," Kim asks opponents of 3D manufacturing, "is using vast amounts of raw materials to produce millions of parts in faraway places like India and China and shipped around the world, a superior model to allowing individuals the freedom and luxury of being able to print out exactly what they need, when they need it, with no waste, at a fraction of the cost?"

Kim is still waiting to hear a good response but, not content to just let the future take its course, she returns to her apartment and prints out a new shirt with the slogan, "The Revolution Will Be Printed."

— BONUS QUESTIONS —

Look around your home or office. What items could be printed with today's technology? What items do you think could be printed with a 3D printer in 2020?

How does the ability of consumers to make things in their home or office affect your business or industry?

What are a few items that you think could never be printed in the future?

Do you think 3D printing will increase or decrease the number of people employed in manufacturing?

Good 3D printers are now being sold for less than $500. What price do you think most consumers would be willing to pay for the ability to print products in their homes? What price would you pay?

Are there additional benefits to 3D printing (reduced transportation and shipping costs, environmental benefits, consumer convenience, etc.) that might facilitate its advance?

Do you think intellectual property laws apply to 3D printing? For example, should you be able to print out a toy based on a Disney character without compensating them in some way?

Upscale restaurants are beginning to experiment with using 3D printers to create highly customized dishes, such as intricately shaped pasta noodles and artistically designed dessert items. How do you feel about eating something that's been printed?

4

A "CLOUDY" FORECAST: THE FUTURE OF HIGHER EDUCATION

In 2002, the Massachusetts Institute of Technology (MIT) began offering all of its undergraduate courses available online for free. In 2009, Trina Thompson sued her alma mater, Monroe College, for $72,000 because she was unable to find suitable employment after receiving a four-year college degree. In 2011, a nationally touted study claimed that 45 percent of college students couldn't demonstrate any increase in knowledge after their first two years of college. Later in the year, the University of the South became the first college in the nation to voluntarily decrease its tuition. It dropped the price by $4,600—or almost 10 percent. Tuition was still $41,400 a year. In 2012, a trio of high profile Massive Open Online Course providers, or MOOCs, began offering free interactive classes from some of the top universities, professors, and experts in the world. Since then, Coursera, edX, and Udacity—and dozens of other MOOCs—have gone on to attract millions of students to their hundreds of high-quality and career-relevant courses and, in the process, are profoundly changing what defines higher education.

The above examples point toward larger structural change in higher education. How knowledge is being disseminated and shared is shifting, the demands and needs of students are changing, learning habits are in flux, and by necessity (albeit slowly) new educational business models are emerging.

Below is a fictional encounter between Megan, a mature-for-her-age high school senior, and her father, a factory line supervisor. Their conversation offers a peek into the cultural, behavioral, and technological changes that will have affected higher education in 2020.

FUTURE SCENARIO

"Are you nervous, honey?"

"Not really," replied Megan.

"Well, then open it," said her father, referring to the notification she just received on her mobile device. It contained a secure link to the results of his daughter's Secondary Education and Vocational Propensity Evaluation, or "SEVtest"—as most students called it.

"I don't know why they couldn't have just provided me with the results as soon as I finished the exam. I know the test scenarios are constantly updated based on my answers, and I'm sure the program had my results as soon as I finished. Maybe it's a psychological thing... an institutional left-over from the days when your SAT or ACT scores arrived by paper mail."

"Just open it," prompted her father. "This is your ticket to a better future."

Megan rolled her eyes. "No, it isn't, Dad. At best, the test scores will help me understand where I should focus my energy. And besides, many of the careers suggested by the test won't even be relevant in a few years because they're not relevant today!"

"Please," replied her father in a tone suggesting his paternal patience was being tried, "open the link." Megan nonchalantly did so and absorbed its content. She showed no emotion.

"Well?" asked her father pensively.

Megan showed him the results and he embraced his daughter in a big hug. "Top Placement Status. You did it! I'm so proud of you." Excitedly, he added, "It even lists 'veterinarian' as one of your top career aptitudes—remember how you always talked about working with animals as a girl? So what are you thinking? Harvard? Stanford? Northwestern? Maybe Colorado State or Minnesota for vet school? You can pretty much write your own ticket!"

Megan said nothing. Following a long pause, she then said, "You're right, Dad, I can write my own ticket."

"That's the spirit!"

"No, Dad, I mean I'm really going to write my own ticket. I'll be getting the rest of my education from Cloud University."

"Cloud University?" replied the father in a confused tone. "I thought taking classes that way was just for students who didn't have any other options. You could go anywhere with your scores!"

"Haven't you been paying attention to the news, Dad? Regular degrees from regular schools don't work anymore. In fact, some universities are even offering low-performing students incentives to quit pursuing certain educational tracks—such as elementary education and law—and instead pursue new fields of study. Traditional universities are lame... I want training to succeed in our rapidly changing world. Most of what you 'learn,' I could find out in seconds in the cloud. I need training in knowing how to use the vast resources that surround me, not useless facts to memorize. I'm going to put together my own degree from the thousands of excellent and free courses now available—and I intend to help others do the same."

"Megan, that's not a serious option. How could you waste all of your hard work just to study online? I mean, why would you even think..."

Before he could go any further, his daughter cut him off. "Look, Dad, I've already received a full year's worth of course credentials by taking advanced placement (AP) courses online."

"I know and I'm proud of you, but you went to school to do it."

"Only partially true—my French and advanced calculus courses were online because my high school didn't have qualified instructors, but I could have just as easily taken my English and chemistry courses online."

Continuing, Megan said, "It might also interest you to know that the reason I performed so well on the SEVtest is because I used an online test prep program that trained me how to think in a way that would help me give the types of answers the test was looking for. It wasn't because I studied endlessly about facts. The classroom-only learning mentality should have disappeared when the personal computer was invented. I'm telling you, it's a waste of money to spend tens of thousands of dollars a year for a traditional education. Plus, who made the rule that four years is somehow the optimum—or magical—length of time to acquire knowledge?"

"But who'll hire you without a formal degree?"

"Accreditation isn't the answer, Dad. It's the problem. Every year millions of college students graduate and are unable to find good-paying jobs because they aren't prepared. What today's best employers care about now is not 'where' you went to school but, rather, how 'well' you perform on their own competence and aptitude tests. Today's colleges aren't preparing students for either one."

"That's not the school's fault."

"Yes, it is, Dad. Most of them are still in the business of providing average students an average education. The degree is barely worth the piece of paper it's printed on. In fact, many degrees now have a negative value because they take so much time and money but return little financial benefit to the student. Most people are just buying an old, stale brand that has outlived its usefulness and no longer provides much in the way of nutritional value. Most universities do little to equip you with the skills that really matter—like intellectual curiosity, adapting to new knowledge, letting go of obsolete knowledge, innovative thinking, and creative problem-solving. Instead, their degree programs are still built based on antiquated models that were developed to produce uniform Industrial Age workers—just about the last thing we need today in the job market!"

"That may be, but with your scores you can go to a prestigious university. Think of the connections and contacts you'll make."

"True, but at what cost? Plus, it won't be those schools that make me a success. I'm responsible for my own success, and I can educate myself for next to nothing."

"But how will you get a job? I wouldn't hire someone without a degree."

"Many entrepreneurial employers are no longer impressed with a mere diploma, Dad. For some of them, a formal degree may even hurt my chances of being hired because they'll think I just wasted four years learning outdated information—and that I'm not resourceful enough to see all of the amazing learning opportunities available now. They want you to demonstrate knowledge and ability—not just show them a piece of paper that cost you or your parents a hundred grand."

"But..."

"Look, Dad, how many times have you changed jobs this

past decade? Five? Six?"

The father nodded his head in agreement.

"And you lost all of those jobs because you were either replaced by automation or because the career you were in ceased to exist due to advancements in technology, right?"

"Yes, but that's because I didn't go to college and didn't have a degree. If I did, I wouldn't have been in those lower-skilled jobs to begin with! That's exactly what I want you to avoid."

"No," replied Megan softly, no longer looking him in the eye. "It's because you weren't able to adapt fast enough and couldn't demonstrate an aptitude for acquiring a new set of skills. The future is only going to accelerate society's need to adapt. New technologies and new industries are emerging almost overnight now and, in their wake, they're leaving jobs—not to mention entire industries—in their dust.

"This is my future, Dad. I'm going to have to survive in a jungle where I'll have to swing from branch to branch every few years—or maybe even months—in order to get my next banana. More likely, I'll have to create my own branch and grow my own bananas. What school is preparing students for my future? What good is a degree for a skill, a job, or an industry that no longer exists?"

The father was silent.

"I'll tell you, no good!" After a pause, Megan then backed off the statement. "Look, Dad, I'll admit that there are a few jobs left that still require a degree from a traditional university. I'll also admit that some schools and some degrees are better than others. I'll even admit that some students—including a few of my friends and classmates—might benefit from a traditional education. But I won't. I'm self-motivated. I want experiential knowledge, because I understand I'll constantly need to invent my own jobs in the future if I want to stay gainfully employed.

"What I learned working with a mentor at the coding academy I attended last summer was more valuable than anything I learned my whole senior year. Plus, I don't care to sit in a huge room with lackluster students, listening to a professor—or more likely a teacher's assistant—who has never worked a job outside of academia in her or his life, talk about skills that were useful in a job environment that existed a decade ago. I'd rather learn from an instructor online who is a leader in her field and can teach me about all of the latest developments—the best professor for each class, teaching about things that I need to know now."

"But what about the social aspects of college? One of the most important things you learn in college is how to interact with different people."

"Really, Dad?" said Megan in a sarcastic tone. "You want me to go into serious debt so I can learn how to interact with people? In case you haven't noticed, there is this little thing called the Internet that has been around since I was born, and I use it all the time to stay in touch with friends and connect with new ones—as well as potential employers."

"I don't know, Megan. Your plan sounds risky."

"What's really risky is spending $100,000 on college with no guarantee of a good job at the end and being four years behind everyone else who created their own path." Megan then paused before adding in a more conciliatory tone, "How about we compromise?"

"I'm listening."

"Here's what I'd like to propose. I want to pursue an entrepreneurial venture at the same time I'm studying. If I haven't learned enough to allow me to earn a living and move out of the house by the time I'm twenty, I'll enroll in a traditional college." With a smile on her face, Megan then added, "Besides, most of my friends' older brothers and sisters that do have a traditional degree have had to move back in with their parents after graduation because they didn't learn any skills that are needed in today's job market. You have nothing to lose except paying for my tuition."

"What exactly do you have in mind?"

"I'm glad you asked. It might please you to know that some friends and I are already developing a new application that delivers customized educational lessons to other motivated self-learners via mobile and wearable devices. We then plan to market the technology to employers who need to upgrade the skills of their employees."

"And who are these friends of yours?"

"People I've gotten to know through various networks," replied Megan. "I met Paul when we helped tutor each other. He helped me with my French, and I helped him with his English. We started talking and we both believe there is a large market for educational tools to help people like ourselves—motivated self-learners—so we reached out to a few other like-minded people.

"To make a long story short, we've partnered with Ajay, a programmer in Bangalore, who has developed an algorithm that rapidly searches video databases to create customized learning experiences by utilizing clips that have been rated the highest by past users. If necessary, the program will translate the videos into the student's native language as well as display the information in a variety of different virtual reality formats.

"Tobius, another programmer, in Norway, has developed an educational assessment tool that further tailors the information so it can be delivered in the format most appropriate for the individual. For example, depending on whether the person feels they learn better visually, auditorily, or kinesthetically—or some combination of the three—the program delivers the lesson plan that will be best understood by the student. My friend Paul is working on a related program that uses voice and facial recognition technology to determine if the person is successfully processing and absorbing the information.

"My role in the venture is to use my knowledge of gaming dynamics to make sure the student can't advance to the next learning module until he or she has either demonstrated a thorough understanding of the concept being presented or earned enough 'experience credits' by participating in programs, courses, lectures, or activities that provide the functional equivalent of traditional classes. My tool will also be designed to access other peer-based learning tools as well as ensure that the student is fully engaged by making the learning enjoyable and, if possible, slightly addictive—like a good video game.

"We then have another teammate—Maria, a data-mining guru, from São Paulo—who is using publicly available data to identify other self-learners to whom we'll market our technology. She's also working on a related program to help identify employers who might use our services."

Her father was astounded at the breadth and scope of the plan. Finally, he mustered up a follow-up question. "And how do you intend to pay for this venture?"

"Without missing a beat, Megan said, "We're crowdsourcing it. We've already lined up $150,000 in microloans from an assortment of people around the world."

The father just shook his head and laughed, "And when will a learning module be available to help middle-aged people like me cope with all this change?"

Megan just smiled. "You'll be fine, Dad. Just remember the future of education isn't learning about something, it's about learning how to fluidly adapt to change. And it's definitely not about going to a physical place to get 'educated'; it's about accessing and curating the ocean of knowledge that already surrounds us in 'the cloud.'"

— BONUS QUESTIONS —

Do you think your children must attend a traditional four-year on-campus university to be successful? If you answered "yes," justify your answer. (For extra credit research "Minerva Project.")

How familiar are you with free educational resources such as Khan Academy, Coursera, EdX, and Udacity, which are already available online?

Think of five careers that existed when you were in high school but no longer exist.

Think of five careers available now that didn't exist when you were in school.

Think of five future careers that may exist by the time today's sixth graders are looking for employment.

What are the implications of employers hiring not based on degrees, but on skills demonstrated on career-specific tests?

Will most students in 2020 physically attend a traditional four-year university or will they become educated another way?

Imagine an elementary school in the year 2020. What is different than today?

Will the proven ability to perform well in customized test scenarios eclipse university credentialing?

How might a range of technologies, such as wearables, Big Data, virtual reality, the Internet of Things, etc., converge to transform the concept of life-long learning?

5

MOVING FORWARD:
THE FUTURE OF TRANSPORTATION

In May of 2014, Google announced that it would be building its own self-driving car. The current model of their new car is small, cute, and can only travel at a top speed of 25 miles an hour, but it points to a future that Google and others want to create—a fleet of on-demand, self-driving "taxis" capable of picking up passengers at the push of a button or the touch of an icon.

In the near future there may be no need to own a vehicle. Having an expensive asset sitting unused 90-95 percent of the time losing value was never a good idea but there just wasn't a better option unless you lived in an area with excellent public transportation. Although we certainly don't expect every car on the road to be self-driving by 2020, we do expect transportation to look far different than it does today.

To help us present our view of the future of transportation, we'll take a look at the activities of 9 year old Sam and his family. Looking at their different perspectives and responses of three generations to the major changes in transportation will give us an insight into how people may adapt to the rapid change in how they move from place to place. Let's join fourth graders Sam and his best friend Sophia playing outside of school just before the bell sounds on their smart devices signaling that class is about to begin.

FUTURE SCENARIO

"Hurry up, we're going to be late for Passenger Ed!" Sophia yelled to Sam from across the playground. It was the last day of their first week of school. Sam ran over to her.

"Let's go—I heard that they're going to teach us how to fight!" Sam replied, mistakenly thinking that the newly added "self-defense" component of the mandatory Passenger Education and Awareness class now being taught in all schools in the state was going to teach him martial arts. (Thanks to recently passed legislation, by 2023, satisfactorily completing the class was required for those aged 10-18 to travel alone on public transportation—other than school buses—or to ride alone in self-driving vehicles.)

As they arrived in the classroom, the pair noticed pictures of horse-drawn carriages and steam engine trains on the large screens behind their teacher. This first week they were receiving a brief history of transportation—from traveling on foot all the way up to present day self-driving vehicles and commercial space travel.

As the teacher began to tell them about how many accidents and deaths had occurred every year before vehicles were required to have safety features such as seat belts and later, vehicle-to-vehicle communication systems, a small girl in the back of the room raised her hand. "If it's so dangerous, why do some people still want to drive? I don't like it when my mom has to take the car off auto-pilot. What if she gets us in an accident?"

Sophia added, with a tone of disapproval, "My bus driver doesn't even do anything... he just sits there and reads. Why do we even need a bus driver?"

Because of their particularly precious cargo, lawmakers in various states had been far more reluctant to grant "autonomous-only" licenses for school buses than they had been for long-haul freight trucks. Shipping companies could now "platoon" their trucks—meaning have them travel closely together in groups—on dedicated cross-country routes in order to save fuel as well as reduce the need for human drivers.

Clearly too young to understand or be saddled with decades of previous driving norms themselves, the children in the class came to an agreement that letting people manually operate an automobile was dangerous and unnecessary. To the teacher, only 25 years old herself, the children's views were surprising. She knew that most young adults didn't like to drive, herself included, but it was incredible to see how fast the younger generations were adapting to the tremendous change happening all around them. Realizing it was time to move on with that day's lesson, the teacher then started a 3D presentation that illustrated the basic self-defense moves that the students would be learning next.

As they walked to their next class, 3D Printing and Design, Sam and Sophia talked about their shared love of space and how they wanted to be on the first manned trip to Mars, which was projected to launch around the time when they would be graduating from high school.

After school, Sam had to take the train because he was going to stay at his father's house for the weekend. His parents had divorced years ago, and his mother, a commercial drone consultant, was attending an out-of-town conference.

During the 28 minute train ride to where he would be getting picked up, Sam began to watch a live stream of the latest rocket launch from India on his smart device. As the sound of the rocket taking off echoed through the train car, he remembered what his teacher had said earlier that day, "A good passenger is always considerate of other passengers," and put in his wireless earpieces so he wouldn't bother anyone around him.

As the train neared the final station, Sam's smart device alerted him of its approach since it had sensed he had fallen asleep. Sam slowly opened his eyes, and looking up, saw his Dad, James, waiting at the station in his new electric car.

"Wow, Dad. This is cool" Sam said, gesturing to the all-touchscreen dashboard. "This is way better than Mom's car–she doesn't even have touchscreens in the windows!"

"Your mom's car is just fine, and anyway, she'll hardly even need it when Google Move starts operating in her town next month." (Sam's city had been selected as one of the first ten test markets to get Google's new service, Move, which was a fleet of on-demand electric self-driving taxis.)

"I wish Move was coming here too–then I wouldn't have had to spend all that money on this new car. It's sure a lot better than that ShareCar app that took my job!"

Sam's dad had lost his job as a taxi driver four years earlier. Car sharing apps had taken away so much of his employer's business that they were forced to dramatically reduce the number of drivers they employed. After years of protests and unsuccessful lobbying by the taxi industry, most taxi companies that refused to adapt to using new routing and scheduling tools went bankrupt.

"You like your new job better anyway," Sam countered, trying to avoid a lengthy discussion about why his dad thought ShareCar was bad for consumers and how it wasn't fair that a teenager could create an algorithm for a car sharing service in a single weekend that would result in the loss of thousands of jobs for cab drivers.

"Yeah, I guess you're right. I would have lost it eventually anyway. Besides, now I'm working with technology, not against it," replied James, who after nine months of online classes had earned a micro-degree and had become an urban planner with a company focused on reclaiming prime land previously occupied by parking lots or under-utilized traffic lanes. (In major urban centers, the proliferation of car sharing services together with the growth of autonomous and semi-autonomous smart vehicles, had significantly reduced the number of automobiles. This, in turn, resulted in many cities choosing to repurpose those spaces for parks, commercial property, housing, and in some cases, vertical gardens to grow food.)

As Sam and James arrived at his house the doors unlocked. The house was already at the temperature they preferred because the car signaled to it that they were on the way and various connected systems and devices prepared the home for their arrival.

As the car parked itself above the charging pad in the garage, James asked, "Did you get assigned any education experience homework for this weekend?" Much of the homework now being assigned in classes was in the form of virtual reality (VR) or VR experiences. Students would don a thin, lightweight, and inexpensive VR headset and take part in historical events or solve problems in a hands-on 3D environment.

"Only one," replied Sam. "For my 3D Printing and Design class, I get to pick a form of transportation and design a single component for it."

"Let me guess... you picked a space ship?"

"How did you know?" Sam joked.

"Just make sure you finish your homework after dinner tonight. Remember, we're going to Grandpa's tomorrow."

The next morning, after being awoken by an alert on his smart device telling him the best time to leave (based on expected traffic patterns and some bad weather moving into the area), James groggily asked it to send a reminder to his dad with the time they were projected to arrive.

Sam's grandpa lived in a retirement community about 30 minutes outside of town, down a long and usually uncongested highway. In 2016, it had been one of the first designated stretches of highway approved for self-driving vehicles and for the use of full auto-pilot. When the predicted thunderstorm arrived, James took advantage of this feature on his new car and let it drive through the heavy rain until they neared their destination. While the car drove, he and Sam used the car's interactive dashboard display to look up more information on Sam's homework assignment.

"Driver re-engage," the car demanded, and a slight vibration in the driver's seat accompanied by a flashing red symbol on the dashboard let James know it was time to retake control of the vehicle. A few moments later, just as they were pulling in to the parking garage, a dog darted in front of them and the car avoided hitting it by maneuvering out of the way just in time.

"Watch out!" Sam yelled a half-second after the car had already averted an accident.

"Wow! That was close! I'm glad I chose to activate the auto-avoidance option this morning!" James exclaimed. "And it's a good thing I did. Not only would the dog have been hurt, but its owner might have sued me for not having it on."

"You can get sued for driving yourself instead of letting the car take over?" asked Sam with a confused look.

"Yeah..." replied James. Always interested in the massive changes in the transportation sector after he had lost his job as a cab driver, James had been following advancements and new laws closely and the differences in each state. "Ever since last year when that guy in California got hit walking in a marked crosswalk and his family filed a suit against the driver, all kinds of new cases are popping up where a human driver caused an accident.

They're arguing that the driver should have been in self-driving mode since it has been proven to be safer than driving yourself."

As they walked up to the apartment, Sam's grandfather was already waiting at the door because the car notified him that they had just parked.

"Hey Sammy! Jimmy! I'm so glad to see you two–It's been too long!"

After giving him a hug, Sam said, "Grandpa, have you seen dad's new car? It has auto-avoidance! It just saved us from hitting a dog!"

After inspecting the new car, Grandpa said, "Jimmy, you're probably not going to believe this, but I just ordered one of those fully self-driving cars. I'm sick of sitting around here waiting for somebody to give me a ride."

Sam's grandpa had been a helicopter pilot in the Vietnam War and was highly self-reliant. His move to the retirement community had been difficult, as had his loss of his driver's license a few years earlier due to a rare condition that was deteriorating his eyesight.

"Who knows how long it will be before Google or whoever gets their vehicles way out here? Plus, I want to be able to keep my fishing gear in there without having to carry it back and forth from the house."

"You, of all people, are getting a self-driving car?" James asked incredulously. "After I lost my job, didn't you start one of the biggest online groups protesting self-driving vehicles? You said that self-driving cars would destroy the economy!" (The group had staged protests in thirty cities throughout the U.S. and Canada to oppose legislation that was paving the way for the legalization of autonomous vehicles. The demonstrations garnered some media attention, but were ultimately unsuccessful in persuading lawmakers.)

"People have a right to be wrong sometimes. I was afraid of what could happen with machines driving alongside people. But now I see now how much better they are. Plus, for people like me that can't drive anymore, they can give us our independence back. Why, I even have a date with a woman I met during one of the protests and as soon as the new car arrives, I plan on picking her up in it."

"Well, I'm happy for you, Dad. I'm glad that you'll be able to get around on your own."

"By the way, Jimmy, did you hear that GM is finally going under? You know my favorite car was that classic '64 Impala two-door hardtop that we had when you were a baby. It makes me sad to think there'll be no more cars like that anymore, although I'll admit that cars today are safer, smarter, and better for the environment. I guess kids these days have no need to own a car and I guess, something's gotta give."

"I bet Sam doesn't want one, do you Sammy?"

Sam, who had been busy scanning his dad's new car with his smart device so he could upload the file to one of the 3D printers at school and print out a toy replica, looked up and rejoined the conversation.

"No Grandpa. Driving looks dangerous. I learned in my class yesterday that people that don't use auto-pilot make the roads less safe for everyone else because they can't pay attention to everything like a computer. We tried out a real-world driving simulator in VR and it was hard to watch out for everything."

"You know, dad," James interjected, "it's not just the kids that don't want to own a car anymore. Now that the roads are getting so much safer from all these self-driving cars, and regular cars with better sensors, if it wasn't for driving you and Sam around I probably would have bought an electric bike to get to work instead."

"That might be good for you, but some of us don't have that option." How about this, Sammy... After my car gets delivered, I'll come over and pick you up so we can go fishing!" You could tell by the look in Grandpa's eyes that he just couldn't wait to get his new car—and regain his freedom to go where he pleased.

"Maybe in a few years, we could rent a self-driving RV and go to that lake I'm always telling you about—the one where the fish are almost begging to be caught. Without the driver's seat, there's all kinds of room in there. It's like a nice apartment on wheels. We can even rent a small freezer to put in it to keep all of the fish we catch. We'll have a great time."

"That sounds fun, Grandpa. And maybe after that we can take it to the National Air and Space Museum in Washington D.C. They have the first commercial spaceship ever flown on display there!"

Still thinking about spaceships, Sam jumped in his dad's car so he could view the Air and Space Museum's new interactive tour on the large dash screen.

With Sam out of earshot, James asked his dad in a concerned tone, "Dad, how are you going to be able to afford the car and the insurance? You know, cars with fully-autonomous mode are going to be expensive to insure for a while until lawmakers and regulators figure out who—or what—is at fault if you get in an accident."

"I know it will be more expensive, for now at least," replied his dad. "But I'm going to get that new insurance that only charges by the mile. Since I'm not going 30 miles into the city to work each day anymore, it shouldn't cost much at all. And now I can even have a few beers at my weekly poker night and not have to worry about driving home. I bet bar owners love these new cars!

"And," he added, "now that everything gets delivered so quickly, I barely have to leave to go buy anything, so that will save me miles too." James thought about it for a minute and realized the cost of insurance might not be such a big deal.

"At least promise me that you'll let me know if it gets to be too much. I know you sure spent enough on my car insurance when I was younger! I'm sure glad that I'm not going to have to worry about Sam trying to race everybody when he gets older, at least not on earth," James joked.

After Sam finished taking the virtual tour of the museum, they walked back to the house together so they could watch the beginning of the 2020 "24 Hours of Le Mans'" race. This year, the first autonomous car was being allowed to compete—much to the distress and protest of many of the human drivers—and was expected to draw a record audience. Sam bet his dad and grandpa a dollar that the new entry, nicknamed Kitt, Jr., would win.

On the ride home after a fun afternoon watching the race, Sam and James passed a small building where James had worked as a teenager.

"Look over there, Sam," James said as he pointed to the building. "That's where I had my first job. I was only a few years older than you," James said, as he realized how fast Sam was growing up. "It used to be a gas station back when all cars ran on gas instead of electricity from batteries or from fuel cells like your mom's car. Now look at it. It seems like they're turning all the gas stations into automated hydrogen fuel dispensers or car-sharing pickup locations. I bet in five or ten years, there won't be any stations that still have regular old gas!"

"Yeah, mom is always saying that there needs to be a hydrogen station near our neighborhood. Lots of people have cars like hers there. Hopefully they'll convert the station by my soccer field into a multi-fuel recharging station. Then everyone won't have to drive so far to get whatever type their car needs," added Sam.

As James reminisced about working at the station, Sam began talking about his ideas for the future of travel and how he and Sophia wanted to be on the first manned mission to Mars.

Despite the fact that there was a mission planned to transport the first four people to Mars in 2029, James wasn't at all convinced that it would happen then. The mission date had already been delayed several times due to unforeseen challenges, and although James didn't want to spoil Sam's fun, he did offer a suggestion.

"That's a great goal, Sam, but I would recommend that you and Sophia wait until a few missions have been completed and they've had time to work all the bugs out. The last place you want to have a breakdown is halfway to Mars!"

Sam thought about it and remembering what his hero Elon Musk once said, "I want to die on Mars, just not on impact," and decided that waiting until after there had been a few successful missions was probably a good idea.

— BONUS QUESTIONS —

How many hours a day does your primary vehicle sit parked?

Can you picture a day when you won't own a vehicle? How do you foresee yourself getting around?

Would you be willing to let strangers rent your car using a car sharing service? Would you ever rent a stranger's car?

Do you own an all-electric car? If not, would you ever consider it?

What do you think will be the primary mode of transportation in the year 2020? What about 2025? Do you think enough people may choose to ride in a self-driving vehicle instead of flying that it will impact regional airlines?

Do you think that children born today will ever need a driver's license?

If self-driving cars become widely used and available, we will need far fewer parking lots and traffic lanes. How might these spaces be repurposed?

Would you be willing to live farther from your job if you owned or had access to a self-driving vehicle? What about living farther from a city center, and from stores and restaurants?

What's your favorite way to travel currently? What do you think it will be in the year 2020?

Do you think the average consumer will ever own a flying car?

6

GROWING UP EVERYWHERE: THE FUTURE OF FARMING

On a 7,000-acre farm in California, a large combine drives itself with sub-meter accuracy and lays down fertilizer only in areas predetermined by the device's yield mapping software to need additional nutrients. Half a world away, on a rooftop in Berlin, Germany, sits an aquaponic farm that produces both vegetables and fish. It uses the fish waste to fertilize the plants, and the plants to purify the water. Both trends, in their separate ways, foreshadow how the agriculture industry will feed the 500 million new people expected to be added to the world's population by the end of the decade. What follows is a glimpse into the world of farming circa 2020.

FUTURE SCENARIO

Using data supplied from the latest private Chinese satellite, as well as information provided from a low-cost unmanned aerial vehicle (UAV), a businessman working for a Russian agricultural conglomerate in Moscow monitors a self-driven combine a thousand miles away on a farm in the Krasnodar region of Russia. The combine steers itself with sub-millimeter accuracy in the middle of the night and disperses tightly controlled amounts of the latest variety of genetically modified corn and soybean seeds in perfectly aligned rows.

So accurate is the GPS and UAV data that the combine retraces its previous trips over the soil with near-perfect accuracy and no land is unnecessarily lost due to soil compaction. The increased accuracy (from sub-meter to sub-millimeter levels) has allowed the conglomerate to squeeze an additional twenty acres of land production for every thousand acres it farms. Comparable yield increases have been experienced elsewhere around the world as many of the precision agricultural tools and prescriptive planting methodologies have become so affordable that even the few remaining midsized farms have incorporated them into their regular farming practices.

Because the conglomerate can access the latest weather forecasting models as well as operate around the clock, it is able to plant its crops at a time optimized for both reducing water usage and ensuring the maximum growth potential of the half-inch of rain expected to begin falling in a few hours. Furthermore, because the precision agriculture technology can be used to plant and space corn and soybeans at an optimal distance from one another, it is able to minimize the use of fertilizers. (This is because the nitrogen from the soybeans benefited the corn.) Planting the two crops together also prevents soil erosion and reduces runoff. It is estimated that five percent of all farmland now employs elements of intercropping or "companion planting."

As significant as the advances in precision farming and prescriptive planting techniques are, they pale in comparison to the continued advances in genomics that pushed the yield of soybeans to 200 bushels per acres and corn to 410 bushels per acre. As farmers around the world reaped similar advances, concerns over feeding the world's surging population dissipated (poverty and starvation still exist, but are caused mainly by ineffective and corrupt political regimes, not food scarcity) and were replaced by concerns over plunging prices caused by supply exceeding demand.

The most significant yield increases were seen in the crops of sugar cane, wheat, corn, soybeans, rice, barley, potatoes, and sorghum. Advances in genetics were not only credited with feeding the additional half-billion new people on the planet, they were also making people around the world healthier. In the United States, certain crops were modified to add Omega-3 to peoples' diets in an effort to reduce the prevalence of heart disease. In India and China, iron was added to certain types of rice to fight against iron-deficiency, and in northern climates of North America and Europe, Vitamin D was added to wheat to counter the negative consequences of a natural lack of sunlight.

So noteworthy were the advances in genomics that by 2019, a number of leading environmental groups had reversed their longstanding opposition to genetically modified organisms (GMO).

"To do otherwise," said Renee LaChappelle, executive director of World Sustainable Land Institute, "would be to relegate millions of the world's poorest citizens to a continued existence of poverty, starvation, and death." LaChapelle went on to add, "The world simply can't afford the luxury of only producing and consuming organically grown crops. They're too water-intensive and spoil too quickly."

A handful of sustainable/organic-related organizations still opposed the policy shift, but they were now a minority and no longer argued that the newer GMO crops didn't use less water or fewer chemical inputs but, rather, were bad because they ceded too much power to the large corporations that produced the seeds.

Officials at the largest ag-bio companies, plus a handful of smaller private genetic start-ups, countered that their technology was necessary if they were to continue to build upon the extraordinary advances achieved in the past decade. Advances, they argued, that were equal to, and in some cases greater than, the improvements witnessed during the "Green Revolution" of the 1960s and 1970s.

Perhaps the greatest of these achievements was the creation of new types of perennial wheat and corn. This advance alone effectively doubled farmers' yields by allowing them to harvest two crops a year, whereas before only one was possible. In a handful of African countries, this breakthrough virtually eliminated the food crisis and was credited with bringing political stability for the first time in decades. As an added benefit, the deep roots of the perennial crops allowed the crops to access the water deeper in the land, thus holding the soil intact and preventing erosion.

Ironically, as more land was being cultivated and growing periods were becoming more pronounced, the amounts of chemical inputs, fertilizers, pesticides, and fungicides, were decreasing. Part of the decrease was due to the creation of genetically modified crops that offered better "natural" protection against certain diseases, funguses, and insects; part could be attributed to the exponential growth of microsensors farmers deployed across their fields to better monitor when and where they needed the chemicals; part due to new nanofiltration systems capable of effectively capturing nitrogen run-off and then recycling the nitrogen into fertilizer, part was the result of continued advances in UAV-assisted field management and other precision farming tools that allowed fertilizers to be prescribed in precisely measured amounts.

Only slightly less significant than the creation of new perennial types of crops in terms of increasing agricultural output was the creation of new types of drought-resistant seeds that could grow in conditions previously not conducive to farming. These advances were especially beneficial to farmers in the increasingly arid regions in California, Australia, northwest China, and sub-Saharan Africa where the effects of climate change were being felt most intensely.

Concerns over insects' and fungi's ability to become resistant to genetically modified crops was still a serious concern, but scientist's ability to employ powerful gene sequencing machines and supercomputers allowed them to create new versions of seeds at a faster pace than Mother Nature could adapt to them. The concern was also being mitigated by the extraordinary advances researchers were making in understanding microbes and then applying that research into effective bio-pesticides.

In a limited number of cases, the combination of the aforementioned advances allowed some farmers to switch from growing crops for food to growing crops for biofuels. In the American southwest, land previously used for fruits and vegetables was transitioned to large algae farms and was now responsible for producing hundreds of millions of gallons of jet fuel. In Brazil, large bioreactors, using only genetically modified organisms, carbon dioxide and sunlight, were producing record amounts of biodiesel on lands previously used to grow sugar cane.

Another consequence of the unexpected increase in agricultural yield was that commodities such as corn and grain that had previously gone directly to the market for individual consumption were redirected toward the cattle and poultry industries as feedstock. This, in turn, allowed the meat and poultry industries to keep pace with the millions of new middle class citizens in Brazil, China, and certain regions in India who were seeking the more protein-rich diets that red meat and chicken provided.

So heavy was the demand that in certain regions a niche market for "in vitro"—or lab-grown—meat had materialized. Scientific and biotechnology advances had reached the point where the taste and texture of many in-vitro meats was now indistinguishable from naturally produced meats. The former was still expensive, but some consumers were willing to pay the higher price because they viewed lab-grown meat as more humane (no animals were slaughtered in its creation) and more environmentally friendly (unlike a cow that must consume an average of 10,000 pounds of feedstock to produce 1,000 pounds of meat, in-vitro meat is created with almost zero waste). A growing number of companies were even beginning to roll out large-scale advertising campaigns to convince people that lab-grown meat was healthier, more flavorful, and better for the environment. In addition to in-vitro meat, another less expensive meat-alternative made from plant proteins was quickly gaining popularity for its affordability, near-meat taste and meat-like "mouth-feel" or texture.

In spite of this extraordinary progress, the world's food situation was far from perfect. One downside of all the additional land being farmed was that, in spite of the creation of a variety of drought-resistant crops, the demand for water continued to increase. Advances in nanotechnology had yielded significant improvements in desalination technology, and continued improvements in solar and tidal power were able to meet the power requirements of the growing number of desalination plants, but, the net effect was that the salinity of the world's oceans continued to rise and this issue was gaining the serious attention of marine biologists and politicians around the world—especially in the Persian Gulf where vast quantities of the brine created by the desalination plants was being dumped back into the sea.

Also, advances in aquatic farming were slow to develop and, in 2018, officials at the United Nations called upon the gov-

ernments of Japan, Indonesia, and the Philippines to severely re-
strict both the number of fishing licenses granted and the areas
those fishermen could operate. So severe was the state of the
world's fisheries that the number of endangered species had qua-
drupled in the past decade. In a handful of cases, the navies of Japan, China, and the United States had been called upon to police
the world's ocean against rogue fisherman who either refused to
have their fishing vessels outfitted with the latest tracking technology, used banned methods, or continued to fish in restricted
areas. In one testy standoff, the Chinese navy fired upon a small
fleet of North Korean ships and set off a dangerous international
incident that caused the militaries in both countries to go on their
highest alert and wreaked havoc on global supply chains as the
world's busiest shipping lane was disrupted for the better part of
two weeks.

It was concern over growing water shortages—more so than
the "acidification" of the world's ocean—that fueled the growth of
agriculture's second big trend: urban farming. As the price of water skyrocketed during the previous decade, farmers, retailers, and
consumers reacted to the change. Farmers responded by planting genetically modified and perennial crops designed to use less
water. They employed more sensors, the latest satellite data, and
drip irrigation systems to accurately gauge exactly where and
when to use water.

Retailers got into the act by demanding suppliers employ
more hydroponic farming techniques in locations closer to major
metropolitan areas. In America, this resulted in underutilized land
in the suburbs being re-devoted to farming. In one of the more
innovative cases, a 100-acre mall outside of Kansas City was torn
down and repurposed to hydroponic agriculture. Through the innovative use of mineral nutrient solutions and water recycling
techniques, the new farm had doubled the yield of a conven-

tional farm. In post-bankruptcy Detroit, the transition was more pronounced because of city and state government leader's willingness to try anything that could help begin to restore the city. Significant amounts of acreage were re-allocated for farming and the Michigan Department of Agriculture began marketing Detroit as "Grow-Town—The New Leader in Urban Agriculture."

In Asia and across the Middle East, a growing number of high-rise apartment and office buildings were dedicating as much as 10 percent of their space to innovative hydroponic farming solutions that required no soil. Advances in water filtration technology and LED lighting made it possible for a surprising number of crops to be grown effectively inside these complexes.

Individual households also began adjusting to the new realities of a water-constrained world. Beset by long-term structural unemployment due to the growth of robotics, additive manufacturing, ever more advanced software and artificial intelligence, as well as innovative open-sourced teaching methods that had decimated the ranks of high school teachers and university professors, more people took to growing food as a way to supplement their shrinking incomes. The University of Michigan started an experimental new degree program targeted at individuals interested in pursuing a career in urban agriculture, while scores of technical colleges offered courses for those people just interested in learning the fundamentals of growing their own food.

In other cases, urban residents, in an effort to cut down on their food bills, utilized new networks to establish more direct relationships with rural farmers that effectively cut out the middleman and allowed farmers to supply consumers with fresh produce and meat directly. Other urban residents repurposed their rooftops, balconies, and small yards into makeshift plots, while suburban residents refashioned their larger yards into mini-farms. In response to continued budget cuts, one major city transformed four of its city parks into community farms and rented out small plots on an annual basis. (To guard against theft, low-cost cameras with motion detectors were positioned around each plot.)

One curious side effect of the transition to urban farming was that a boutique market in the insurance industry was created to offer small urban farmers protection against the vagaries of Mother Nature. Hard hit by the rapid advancements in self-driving cars and the related drops in revenue, insurance companies were eager to find new ways to offset those losses. Depending upon the location of the farm and the types of crops being grown, policies could be purchased for as little as five dollars, which allowed just about anyone with an urban farm to purchase a policy.

In ways small and big, the agriculture industry and hundreds of thousands of new "urban farmers" rose to the challenge of feeding the world's surging population with a healthier and more protein-rich diet in a way that was also more sustainable than past practices. The big question was whether farmers, citizens and agri-business could repeat their accomplishments in the coming decade and feed the 600 million new mouths expected to arrive by 2030.

— BONUS QUESTIONS —

In the US, the percentage of the population working in agriculture has dropped from over 40 percent in 1900 to below 2 percent in 2002. Will we ever reach a point when food production becomes fully automated and requires no human labor?

Do you believe the terms "precision agriculture" and "prescriptive planting" will still be in use by 2020, or will all farmers just be assumed to be using "precision" and "prescriptive" techniques and those terms will fade from use?

What are the benefits of genetically modified crops? What are the negative aspects?

In August 2013, lab-grown meat was used to make a hamburger which was cooked and eaten in front of an audience in London. It took a decade of trial and error to create this burger, and at a cost of several hundred thousand dollars. Once the price drops to consumer-level affordability, what will it take for most people to accept this new process of meat production?

It's been often said that the next world war will be fought not over oil or land, but over water. Do you think we can develop technologies to produce enough drinking water before the lack of it starts a serious global conflict?

Climate change is already affecting agriculture and crops around the world. In 2020, do you think we will have a found a way to largely reverse—or, at least, begin to counter—its effects?

Do you think it will ever be economical and convenient enough to grow all of your own food at home—or at least locally?

Would you be interested in living in a building that had indoor gardens and allowed residents to purchase fresh vegetables and other produce at an affordable price and with a greatly reduced environmental impact?

7

SHIFTING POWER:
THE FUTURE OF ELECTRICITY

FUTURE SCENARIO

In the spring of 2016, the largest solar flare to affect North America in more than one hundred years caused a geomagnetic storm that disabled hundreds of transformers and transmission lines across the United States and Canada. In the ensuing weeks, an estimated fifty million citizens were stranded without electricity and in a few remote areas it was a full month before consistent power was restored. The event resulted in 15,000 deaths, mainly due to the fact that emergency backup generators at scores of hospitals across the country were unable to operate for more than a few days, and many life support devices weren't able to function. The catastrophe dealt a serious blow to the global economy as thousands of businesses went idle. Conservative estimates placed the economic damage at $2 trillion—more than sixteen times the direct economic cost of the 9/11 terrorist attacks.

In the aftermath of the crisis, politicians, regulators, and citizens demanded to know, "How could this happen?" A few, more farsighted individuals asked, "What did we learn from this event and how can we prevent it from happening again?"

The scene described below takes place at a board meeting of a regional utility cooperative in the Midwest. The board is preparing a strategic plan for the year 2020. The main protagonists are Dylan, the cooperative's progressive forty-year-old executive director, and Edgar, the board's more conservative-thinking chairman. The former is new to his responsibilities, while Edgar has served as chair for fifteen years. Positioned between the two men is Miriam, a utility industry consultant who has been charged with facilitating the board's strategic planning session. The following discussion takes place after the board has heard from a series of industry experts discussing "Smart Grid" and "Internet of Things" developments as well as the latest advances in battery technology, electric cars, software, sensors, super-conductive transmission wires, solid-state transistors, and developments in renewable energy for both commercial and residential customers.

Miriam began the afternoon's final session by addressing Dylan and Edgar.

"You both agree that the utility industry can't return to business as usual. Even many conservative and traditional-thinking industry groups are predicting the eventual demise of the large utilities, unless we recognize and respond to the dramatic changes now underway. You also agree significant steps need to be taken in order to make the grid more reliable. That's good. The bad news is your respective visions of the near-term future are so different that compromise might be difficult. I suggest we focus first on the broad areas of agreement—the low-hanging fruit, if you will. Next, we'll turn to the more controversial areas and let both of you spell out your respective views for the other board members. We'll then take a vote on the strategic direction of the utility."

"From our earlier discussion," continued Miriam, "it's clear we can agree that consumers have become more efficient in their use of electricity. If there's a silver lining to the solar flare outage it's that users have become sensitized to conserving energy. What's more is that all of the major appliance manufacturers have accelerated their plans to make their refrigerators, dishwashers, washing machines and dryers compliant with various connected device standards such as ZigBee Smart Energy 1.2 by the end of next year, which should further accelerate the push toward energy conservation by allowing customers to monitor and control their energy usage on these new appliances."

"I agree," said Edgar, "and let's not forget LED lights. They continue to become better and less expensive. Home energy usage should further continue to drop as a result. I also think the consumers will use these smart appliances and other networked devices in their homes and offices to make better decisions about when, for example, they run their air conditioners in the summer or how long they operate their humidifiers in the winter." Edgar then paused before adding, "But we can't count on smart meters to deliver the long sought-after promise of 'dynamic' or 'real-time' pricing. For that to take place, we'll need state regulators across our region to agree to the required installation of the devices. Past experience tells us that neither regulators, politicians, nor our customers trust that the smart meters will deliver lower prices. What's more, a surprising number of folks still believe the devices can cause brain cancer or are yet another invasion of their privacy. We can't count on smart meters taking root. At least not in our part of the country."

"I disagree," said Dylan, "and I'm confident we can lead the way. In fact, I'd like to propose we hire an interactive software designer with a specialty in gaming dynamics to help us figure out how our customers can use their mobile devices to better monitor and control their home energy usage through the smart meters and home automation. Even if the technology lowers their electricity usage by just five percent, in just our markets that'd be equal to not having to produce more than 1 Gigawatt annually—or the equivalent of not building a half-dozen midsized coal-power plants. We need to focus on conservation first." Dylan then emphasized his point by adding, "The most efficient power plant is the one we never need to build."

"Have you looked at our demographics?" snapped Edgar. "Most of our customers are fifty-five or older, and they aren't tech-savvy. There's no way they're going to embrace smart meters, real-time pricing, or gaming dynamics—whatever the hell that is."

"We need to get serious about building some new next-generation, natural gas-fired power plants," continued Edgar.

"We need to get serious about focusing on 'negawatts,'" replied Dylan. "The cleanest energy is energy which is conserved, and as a result never produced."

At this point, Miriam stepped in to mediate. "You both agree, though, that many of your larger industrial customers, such as the grocery chains, are willing to utilize demand response technology to control their energy consumption during periods of peak usage in return for substantial savings. It seems that any technology that can help produce 'negawatts' makes sense. Also, industry forecasting tools are continuously improving and new data-mining business intelligence technologies and business analytical tools are helping us determine which customers to target for these new services."

Dylan nodded his head in vigorous agreement. Edgar was noncommittal, and responded by saying, "Yeah, that's true for our industrial customers, but I'm talking about our residential customers who make up half of our business."

Dylan pursed his lips, shook his head and countered with, "You're asking the wrong question with regard to our older customers. You're asking: 'Will they employ smart meters while using gaming dynamics?' But rather the question you really need to be asking is: 'Do our customers want to save money?' The answer to that is a resounding 'yes'—especially among the very customers you are talking about, Edgar. Our more elderly customers' views about money were instilled by parents raised during the Depression. They value every penny, and if a new device can deliver real savings they'll embrace it."

"I'll believe it when I see it," said Edgar in a dismissive tone.

Not one to back down, Dylan shot back, "The fastest-growing demographic among video-gamers are people fifty-five and older. Why? I'll tell you why: Because many of the new games are so easy and intuitive that they can now play them with their grandchildren—they're playing games on their newly purchased smart phones and tablets, and now many of them are even beginning to buy virtual reality headsets! My point is that if a technology is simple enough—and if it saves money—people will embrace it."

Catching his breath, Dylan then added, "And if you look closely at the most successful electronics retailers and manufacturers, after the success of smart thermostats, they are beginning to design and sell other home energy saving tools such as 'plug-and-play' micro wind turbines, portable solar panels and smart windows. They're making these devices attractive and easy to use and install. As more people begin to understand they're protecting both the environment and their pocketbooks, the market for these products is going to skyrocket! Who knows: Our greatest challenge in the near future might not be a scarcity of fossil fuels but an abundance of renewable energies. Plus, as our customers continue to conserve more and more electricity and are employing more renewable energy sources to generate power, we may be forced to charge higher rates to our remaining customers—making those behaviors increasingly more attractive to our dwindling customer base. It could become a vicious downward cycle. We need to start looking at other options before it's too late!"

"Okay. Everyone keep their cool," interjected Miriam. "Let's keep this conversation moving forward. Over the past few days, we've heard from a number of experts telling us solid-state transformers and new high-temperature superconducting transmission lines have reached a price point where utilities can begin installing them on a large-scale basis."

"That's right," said Edgar. "If smart meters are the brains of the smart grid, and I'm still not convinced they are, solid-state transformers are the muscle. They are going to allow us to more efficiently and effectively convert the direct current power from the new power plants we need to build to the alternating current our customers use; and the new wires will dramatically reduce on 'line loss.' These are two areas we definitely need to make a strategic investment."

"Not so fast," said Dylan breaking in. "I agree we need to make a strategic investment in both solid-state transformers and new transmission lines, but not for the reasons you suggest. We should be investing in solid-state technology because it'll allow us to more effectively handle inputs from the growing number of renewable energy sources beginning to pop up everywhere, such as community solar farms, solar-collecting windows, and natural gas operated fuel cells. More significantly, solid-state transformers are going to allow for the bi-directional transfer of power between consumers as well as help us engage in more efficient dynamic pricing. In short, these devices are going to facilitate the creation of new business models that we need to take advantage of."

"Such as...?" chided Edgar.

"I don't exactly know yet...maybe prepaid electricity plans. If a customer can only afford to budget one hundred dollars a month for electricity, they might be more willing to agree to a smart meter or a smart device that can help them operate their appliances when energy is available at affordable prices.

"I do know that if people can begin producing their own energy from highly efficient solar cells, low-cost fuel cells, and better generating wind turbines and then store that excess power in high storage capacity batteries or convert it to hydrogen for use later, we need to figure out how to play in this future! Solid-state transformers are going to allow citizens to harness the excess power they create from their wind turbines and solar panels and sell it to their neighbors. What's our role in this new future?"

"Stop right, there," replied Edgar, raising his voice. "You just made a number of assumptions in that last statement. Look, I understand you think climate change is real, and that the world needs to move toward renewable energy, but we just experienced a massive and tragic electricity outage last year and no one—and I mean no one—wants to revisit that experience. The public expects reliable low-cost electricity. The only known sources that do that are coal, natural gas, nuclear, hydro, and, in some limited cases, wind. We need to focus on building newer, cleaner natural gas plants and some nuclear plants—not worry about how Farmer Joe can sell his excess wind power to Citizen Sally."

"Now it's my turn to question assumptions," interjected Dylan. "First, my emphasis on renewable energy has little to do with my personal concerns over climate change, which, by the way, I share with almost every credible scientist in the world, and everything to do with economics. Advances in nanotechnology, such as those made recently with carbon nanotubes and perovskites, are poised to make solar power a better option than coal for many small residential houses by 2017—not in 2020 or 2030, but next year! Second, advances in material science and 3D printing are allowing for the creation of new wind turbines that have smaller form factors and can operate at lower wind speeds. Third, the fact that three companies are now selling low-cost fuel cells at a profit—without relying on any government subsidies—suggests they're a real threat to the status quo. Fourth, the number of companies and businesses either constructing new net-zero energy buildings or retro-fitting existing buildings to become hyper energy-efficient is growing exponentially. Finally, new high storage, grid-capable batteries that can handle more than 25,000 recharges will soon be on the market and new hydrogen splitting advancements are adding a whole new way to efficiently use intermittent sources like wind or solar. These devices will allow us to store the energy produced from the wind turbines on windy days and from solar farms on sunny days, and then use that energy when the wind isn't blowing or it's cloudy. They'll also allow Farmer Joe to do the same. These devices will take the variability out of renewable energy sources. Distributed, decentralized energy is here, now.

"Moreover," continued Dylan, "whether you agree with my analysis or not, you need to know a couple of things. In Germany, 75 percent of all renewable energy is produced by public citizens, not the utility industry. And they're far from the only country making significant investments in renewables. Germany's reality might very well be our reality. There are also companies out there who understand these numbers and are willing to assume the upfront cost of producing, installing, and maintaining solar cells, wind turbines and fuel cells in exchange for locking customers into fixed contracts below the price we are selling electricity. The bottom line is that these new businesses don't require their customers to put down any money on capital expenditures. They are taking the risk out of purchasing renewable energy. How do you get around this new type of competition? Also, how do you get around the fact that there are now a growing number of cities and communities around the world aggressively pursuing "net-zero" carbon emission goals—and they're doing it not by relying on nuclear power but on renewable energy sources?"

By this time Miriam had lost control of the discussion and decided it best to let both Dylan and Edgar air their arguments without interruption and work afterwards to see what agreement, if any, was possible. If that happened, Miriam thought to herself that the two men's agreement on solid-state transistors, superconducting wires and "negawatts" might be a good place to start.

"I get around that reality by reminding you we've been hearing about these advances for years and nothing, and I mean nothing, has ever come from them! How do you explain the fact that 90 percent of the electricity produced in this country still comes from coal, natural gas, and nuclear?"

"I can explain it," replied Dylan, "by reminding you that when change happens, it happens fast. In 1850, the leading source of oil was from whales. The whaling industry couldn't fathom a different way of doing things. A decade later they were obsolete because of the discovery of oil in the fields of Pennsylvania.

"In the early 2000s, the publishing industry couldn't conceive people would ever warm to the use of electronic books. Today, more than 70 percent of all sales are ebooks. And, in 2010 the automobile industry couldn't imagine hundreds of thousands of young consumers would be utilizing their social networks and other location-based tools to engage in car sharing services that would cannibalize many of their sales. Less than five years later it's a reality, and the first of the three major US automobile companies will probably go bankrupt in late 2017 or early 2018...only this time the government isn't going to step in and bail them out."

"Look," continued Dylan, "every industry thinks it's different; that it's somehow unique and doesn't need to change. Well, I hate to say this but there's nothing special about electricity, and if it can be produced and transmitted more effectively and sold at more reasonable rates, it will be.

"We've been the most effective and efficient conduit for the production and transmission of electricity for more than 100 years, but so what? Our past success is no guarantee of continued future success."

In a more peaceful and conciliatory tone, Dylan concluded by saying, "The one thing I know is that we must change. The nature of how electrical power is being produced, distributed, and consumed is changing and so must we. I think we'd all be wise to recall the saying: 'It is not the strongest of the species that survives, nor the most intelligent; it is those most able to adapt.' Our industry needs to adapt now or we're going to go the way of the Dodo bird, just like the whaling, publishing, and automobile industries."

— BONUS QUESTIONS —

The price of solar power has dropped dramatically in the last few years, now even nearing or surpassing price-parity with fossil fuel produced energy in many areas. How much would you be willing to spend up front on solar panels for your home or business if they provided a per-watt savings?

If battery technology continues to improve (in terms of both price and performance), how might that change the viability of renewable energy resources such as wind and solar?

Although electric vehicles were some of the first vehicles ever produced in the late nineteenth century, over one hundred years later we are now just beginning to see the introduction of hybrid and full-electric vehicles into most auto manufacturer's model lineups. Recent sales figures and growing public interest in the all-electric car company Tesla Motors suggest that purchasing an electric vehicle may soon finally be considered a viable option for many consumers. When do you think non-gas powered vehicles will become the majority of cars on the road?

If 25 percent of all automotive vehicles are electric by 2020, what impact could that have on both electricity production and the grid?

If a majority of homeowners began producing at least fifty percent of their own electricity at home (via solar cells, fuel cell technology or micro wind turbines), how would your business be impacted?

Does your home or business have a "smart meter" that allows you to track your usage throughout the month instead of waiting for your bill to see what you've used?

How do you stay abreast of emerging technologies such as solid-state transformers, advanced batteries and sensors, and developments in renewables such as solar and wind power?

Is there any scenario under which energy abundance—and not scarcity—would become a greater issue for you and your business?

8

A TAILORED FIT:
THE FUTURE OF RETAILING

In the summer of 2011, Tesco, a British retailer, implemented an interesting pilot project in Seoul, South Korea. Because the price of land in the South Korean capital was so expensive, Tesco created an experimental virtual store on the walls of a subway station. The retailer posted a visual display depicting items on a grocery shelf and allowed passengers, using their smartphones, to select products for purchase as they waited at the subway stop. By day's end, the items were delivered to their homes. The experiment resulted in 10,000 shoppers taking advantage of the convenient opportunity and Tesco increasing online revenues in South Korea by 110 percent. This project offers a sneak peek into tomorrow's customizable retail shopping experience.

What follows is a futuristic scenario from the day after Thanksgiving in the Year 2020. The protagonist is Brittany, a twenty-nine-year-old woman who works as a professional "remote" nurse in the Veteran's Administration Virtual Intensive Care Unit where she is responsible for interacting with forty patients in their homes. Today, however, she has the day off and has one thing on her mind—shopping.

FUTURE SCENARIO

"Five, four, three, two, one... Happy Shopping!" At the moment the clock struck midnight and Thanksgiving Day gave way to "Black Friday"—once again the most .profitable day in the retail industry, as many previous "Cyber Monday" shoppers started shopping for the best deals online on Friday instead of waiting until the following week. On Brittany's eighty-four-inch Ultra High Definition Display were three deals that her personal artificially intelligent assistant (PAIA)—a software program that had been learning Brittany's unique tastes and shopping quirks since she first installed it on her all-devices account in 2015—determined she would be most interested in considering. The first item was a pair of casual sandals. Initially, Brittany scoffed at the footwear and said to her PAIA, which she had named AIM-e, (which stood for "Artificially Intelligent Me").

"Really?"

Without responding to her question or sarcastic tone, AIM-e mentioned that the shoes were made of a flexible, breathable, electronic canvas that allowed the product to morph, chameleon-like, into an array of different colors and patterns. Without delay, AIM-e assembled a series of photos and video clips from Brittany's "Life-Log" (a database of personal video recordings Brittany had been using to document her life over the past few years) and showed how the shoes would mix and match with a surprising number of items in her existing wardrobe.

"Cool," she replied, now understanding why AIM-e had selected the shoes. "What's the price?"

After stating that they were $69.95, AIM-e discovered an unadvertised manufacturer promotion and informed Brittany that if she could persuade three of her friends to buy the same pair within the next ten minutes, they would each receive an additional ten dollar discount. Upon Brittany's voice command,

AIM-e estimated it would need to send an invitation to at least six friends if Brittany was to stand a solid chance of partaking in the deal. AIM-e immediately identified a list of those contacts in her social network most likely to be both interested in the deal and still awake (AIM-e did this by noting who was active on their networks during the past few minutes). It then contacted the PAIAs of those individuals and inquired if their owners were interested in the offer. Within minutes, AIM-e's calculations had proven correct, and Brittany and three of her friends had scored their first deal of the 2020 holiday shopping season.

On her large wall-sized screen were now displayed twelve different websites and live feeds. A scene in the upper right-hand corner caught Brittany's attention and she requested it be placed on the full screen. Brittany asked AIM-e what she was looking at and was told it was a scene taking place in Helsinki. Due to the Finland's more stringent retail rules, stores there were not allowed to open until 8:00 a.m.—or midnight on the East Coast of the United States.

"What are all the people lining up to buy?" asked Brittany. AIM-e replied that Nokia-Mobility had succeeded in creating the first truly thin-film, transparent, and wearable mobile computing device. The product was flexible enough to be worn as a bracelet or band, and could also be folded up into the shape of a PMD or stretched into a larger display.

"What else can it do?" Brittany asked in an intrigued voice. She was shown a one-minute promotional video. Afterwards, Brittany knew it'd make the perfect gift for her boyfriend, but needed to know the price and whether it would be available in time for Christmas. When informed of the price, Brittany scrapped the idea. The manufacturer, she was told, was artificially limiting supply to create demand and buzz. By the growing size of the crowd, it was evident they had succeeded. Brittany asked AIM-e to monitor sales and let her know when it might become available at a price that would fit her projected budget. Drawing on an open-source data mining database of past retail information, AIM-e calculated that there was a 40 percent chance it would be available by Valentine's Day at a price she could afford.

Not to be deterred by one minor setback, Brittany returned to the wall display and asked, "What else do you have that might interest me?" In a flash, AIM-e displayed a new blouse it thought would make an affordable gift for Brittany's best friend. Using a series of cameras positioned at the corners of the screen, the blouse was then displayed in 3D. In rapid succession, it was then matched with a combination of pants and jeans AIM-e had scanned from her best friend's network profile. "Do you prefer a certain color for your friend?" asked AIM-e.

Unsure of herself, Brittany asked to be put in contact with two friends who also knew her best friend—and who she also knew she wouldn't be disturbing at this hour—and asked for their opinions. Moments later, the three were gathered in a virtual conference. After reviewing the 3D images, one offered that the collar wasn't her friend's style, while the second asked her own PAIA to confirm whether the friend liked wool. A search of the friend's public profile revealed that she had an allergy to wool. The purchase was scratched and AIM-e learned another fact about Brittany's best friend which it automatically added to that friend's profile. Brittany signed off on the conversation by thanking her friends—and their PAIAs—for saving her $100 on a gift that would have had to be returned. A few years earlier, Brittany would have also reminded the friends of the party she was throwing in less than twenty-four hours, but she knew that would be unnecessary since AIM-e would confirm their attendance with their virtual assistants.

Next up, Brittany asked AIM-e for some recommendations

for her brother who was always tough to buy for because he was a staunch environmentalist with a strong anti-establishment bent. Any product that had even the slightest negative impact on the environment could set him off on a lengthy diatribe as would any mention of what he referred to as the 'Sinister Seven'—Google, Apple, Facebook, Amazon, IBM, Microsoft, and Kovista (an Indian integrated communications provider that didn't even exist until 2015)—who he felt, in his words, "had created an oppressive oligarchy controlling and manipulating global information."

Soon, however, with AIM-e's helpful assistance, Brittany had discovered an innovative agricultural seed bank that was donating a variety of long-forgotten maize seeds to indigenous peoples in Africa and South America. Although these seeds were not as productive as many newer types of genetically modified seeds, a growing number of scientists were concerned that insects were evolving to be super-resistant to the current genetic crop modifications used to keep them away and could leave millions of genetically modified maize fields vulnerable to infestation. The natural diversity of ancient types of maize offered a hedge against such a disaster.

Upon learning the seeds were hand-delivered to the indigenous people by a botanist who spoke the native language, Brittany exclaimed to AIM-e, "Perfect! Let's see my brother not like this year's gift."

The time was only 12:30 a.m. and already Brittany had her most difficult to shop for person, her brother, scratched off her 2020 holiday shopping list. She went to sleep knowing that the remainder of the day's other tasks, shopping for her annual "Holiday Ball," which she hosted for her old high school friends, and organizing the itinerary for her and her grandmother's traditional "CyBrick Monday downtown shopping extravaganza" (created in 2017 to win online shoppers back to brick-and-mortar stores)—

would be a breeze.

After six hours of rest, Brittany was gently awakened by her LED alarm clock that coordinated with the LED lights in her room to simulate the natural light of the sun rising. Next, she took a long, guilt-free hot shower knowing the recycled and purified rainwater had been heated by the solar energy capturing windows of her apartment complex. Afterwards, she grabbed a light breakfast of toast and "Fake-on"—or lab-grown bacon. As a vegetarian, Brittany did not eat animal meat, but she did allow herself the rare (and still pricey) treat of an occasional piece of synthetic meat. Ready for her long day of shopping, Brittany located the closest all-electric car-sharing service vehicle, and drove into the city to meet her grandmother.

Due to all the real-time navigation and enhanced routing technology embedded in the automobile, Brittany arrived ten minutes earlier than she expected because she was able to avoid the most congested routes. As she left the vehicle, her personal mobile device (PMD) automatically paid the car-sharing service, which then changed the car's status to "available" and updated its current location.

Brittany used the extra time to stroll around the shopping district. As she passed a boutique retailer, a location-based automated marketing service detected her presence and sent an alert to her PMD notifying her she was eligible for a 50 percent discount off long-stemmed wine glasses. Realizing she would need a few extra glasses for her party that evening, Brittany entered the store and picked up the product and left. The retailer's radio frequency identification (RFID) system deducted the purchase from her banking account and automatically forwarded the receipt to her virtual file cabinet in the cloud. (At the end of the month, Brittany would receive a visual report documenting how and where she spent her money.)

Next, Brittany visited a virtual store in a "pop-up shop" that was temporarily located in small office space previously used to house a kidney dialysis facility (it had been put out of business by a series of breakthrough treatments for diabetes over the past decade). Inside, the logos of twenty different stores were displayed. With a single voice command, the shelf space of any one of the stores could instantly be called up. Brittany opted to do some virtual shopping at the large all-organic store even though it was physically located less than a mile from her apartment.

With the assistance of AIM-e, Brittany decided to start by selecting the appetizers for that evening's party. Rather than overwhelm her with forty different types of cheese, the virtual shelf displayed only three types. The algorithm behind the display understood that while most people claimed to want more choices, the reality was that too many selections overwhelmed the typical shopper. Moreover, because Brittany was a regular customer, based on her past purchases, the algorithm could estimate her preferences and recommend options she would most likely choose. Brittany selected two of the recommended cheeses and then inquired if the display could recommend a cheese her lactose-intolerant friend might be able to enjoy, as well as one for a vegan friend. The display recommended a goat cheese from northern Italy for the first friend, but failed to find a suitable selection for the latter.

Moving on, Brittany next selected the olives. Picky about the types of chemicals used on her food, she wanted only olives from farms capable of documenting their sustainable practices and organic pedigree. When shown how much more expensive the organic olives were, she balked. Then, figuring it was the only dinner party she'd be throwing the rest of the year, she decided to splurge.

On a whim, Brittany decided to try a new type of corn chip

made with a unique blend of Sri Lankan and Columbian spices. This unlikely combination may have never been tried had it not been for a new "flavor creator" crowdsourcing platform the chip company made available to the public the previous year to help them discover new seasonings for their products. It allowed individuals to create their own sample chips and share them with friends. This particular chip was one of the few that had generated enough interest to be made into a commercial product. Upon selecting the chips, AIM-e presented her with a discount off a new salsa from Brazil. It noted that 60 percent of the people who had previously purchased those particular chips also bought this brand of salsa and had given it an approval rating of 87 percent. Brittany purchased the salsa. Over the years, she had come to trust the combined recommendations of thousands of strangers over branded advertising and the opinions of individual food critics.

Next, Brittany selected her vegetable tray. She began by asking the virtual wall to display only products grown within a 100-mile radius of her apartment. Not only did she prefer the fresher taste of locally grown vegetables, Brittany enjoyed supporting local farmers and reducing her carbon and water footprint. AIM-e estimated that by buying all local products, including carrots grown at a nearby vertical farm, she'd emit 120 fewer pounds of carbon dioxide but use ten more gallons of water. The latter was because the organic vegetables consumed more water than genetically modified crops. Rationalizing that since she had used recycled rainwater for her shower that morning she still had a net-positive "water balance" for the day, Brittany went ahead and bought the more water-intensive organic veggies. Brittany did this because she was still convinced that organic vegetables tasted better, even though every independent taste test in recent years had shown that the latest generations of genetically modified vegetables were preferred by a majority of consumers due to the fact that every variable affecting taste, texture, and appearance was controlled.

Last, but not least, Brittany had to select the wine. Unable to recall the name of the tasty pinot noir she had recently sampled at a friend's house, Brittany used the only information she could recall and asked AIM-e to find the name of the wine from the vineyard owned by the female CEO who had refused to take her company public because she didn't want to subject her company to the short-term whims of Wall Street investors. Told the answer was "Thoreau Farms," Brittany purchased five bottles.

On the other side of the country, her purchase was instantly registered and a robotic device pulled ten bottles from the cellar shelves to ensure that the inventory at the regional distribution center would remain sufficiently stocked throughout the holiday season. (The robots pulled the additional bottles because a high-speed data analytics program calculated Brittany's purchase would create an additional five sales from her friends.)

Upon the company's request, Brittany's wearable PMD displayed a message asking whether she would like to have five percent of the profits from her purchase donated to a viticulture program aimed at educating women in South America. Brittany responded in the affirmative and remembered that the taste and aroma weren't the only thing she enjoyed about Thoreau Farms wines.

With her grocery shopping done, Brittany issued a voice command to have the products delivered to her apartment in a ninety-minute window between 5:30 and 7:00 that evening.

Brittany's PMD alerted her that her grandmother had just departed the subway station and was now only a few blocks away from their favorite cafe. AIM-e asked Brittany whether she would like it to order cups of their favorite coffees. Told yes, AIM-e did so and wirelessly paid for the purchase. When Brittany and her grandmother arrived at the bistro, the warm drinks were waiting for them along with a complementary piece of biscotti.

After some time spent catching up with one another, Brittany prompted the pico-projector on her PMD to display a map of the downtown area and asked AIM-e to propose a personalized shopping tour that would maximize the number of shops they could hit during their eight-hour shopping spree. A week earlier, AIM-e, knowing this day was scheduled, had also booked a lunch reservation at her grandmother's favorite Italian restaurant.

First up was a gift for Brittany's mother. Although she could have easily purchased the sweater online, Brittany had come to appreciate how many retailers now had made the in-store shopping experience extremely pleasant. The lighting, the aromas, the music, the unexpected layouts and, above all else, the personal attention made "in-person" shopping an intimate and fun experience.

Upon arriving at their first destination, the concierge had already pulled many of the sweaters Brittany had previously viewed online for her mother and had them tastefully arranged with a combination of silk scarves designed to accent the various sweaters. After feeling the fabric of each item, Brittany and her grandmother exchanged a knowing glance and pointed to the same sweater-scarf combination. "If you get the sweater, I'll get your mother the scarf," said her grandmother.

The concierge offered to help with more gifts but Brittany and her grandmother had other ideas. As they were walking to the next establishment, a digital display featuring some customized jewelry caught Brittany's eye. Sensing her gaze had stayed on the advertisement long enough to suggest serious interest, the facial recognition technology inside the display changed the sign to read "Emily's Handcrafted Work is available just down the street." The display began to show live footage of Emily working on a piece of customized jewelry. Inside the store a beep from her two-way video display notified Emily that an interested customer was watching her work. Looking casually into the camera, Emily smiled and, holding up a piece of her jewelry, said to Brittany, "If you're interested, come on down and I'll show you and your mother what else I'm capable of doing." Pleased at the overt compliment to her grandmother's youthful looks, the pair agreed to take a detour from their planned itinerary.

"This is what I love about shopping downtown, the serendipity," said her grandmother. Without Brittany's knowledge, AIM-e sent a notice to the Italian restaurant moving back the pair's lunch reservation by fifteen minutes.

Unable to afford regular retail space in the city, Emily had rented a small booth that allowed her to set up shop and sell her customized jewelry on one of the city's busiest sidewalks. The zoning change the city passed in 2018 allowed Emily and scores of other independent artists the opportunity to make a living while also providing the city an additional source of much needed revenue. To maximize taxes, the city rented out different corners based on foot traffic and proximity to major retailers.

Impressed with Emily's work, Brittany's grandmother showed the artist a photo of a pendant her own grandmother had given her decades ago and asked if she could design and print a copy with a few personalized changes. After the photo was transferred to Emily's virtual reality headset she configured a 3D design and asked the grandmother if it resembled the original. Assured that it did, Emily indicated she could design the pendant to the grandmother's specifications and have it made with her 3D printer by the time their shopping spree was done.

The grandmother just shook her head and turned to her granddaughter and said, "If our shopping experience continues to be this easy, we'll be able to catch the opening performance of *The Nutcracker.*"

"Or, we could just get more shopping in," replied Brittany with a smile.

— BONUS QUESTIONS —

Major movie rental companies, large chain bookstores and big electronics outlets have all declared bankruptcy in the past few years. What additional retail establishments do you think might go under in the coming decade, and why?

Are you willing to sacrifice privacy to receive discounted offers? Do you believe the majority of consumers share your view?

What types of clothes and materials do you think we will be wearing in 2020? Will we still dress much like we do today?

Would you let a virtual personal assistant do your shopping for you? Would you also encourage it to inform you of an item you should _not_ buy?

Do you think you would ever trust the recommendation of a virtual personal assistant more than a recommendation given by your best friend?

Do you think society will become more or less materialistic in the coming decade?

As the Internet and social networking platforms are making it easier than ever for friends and neighbors to share and rent everything from lawnmowers and snow blowers to automobiles and even bedrooms in their homes, how do you think such trends (e.g. the "sharing economy," "collaborative consumption," etc.) will alter consumer purchasing habits in the years ahead? What are the implications for retailers?

9

CRIME BY DESIGN:
THE FUTURE OF LAW ENFORCEMENT

In the fall of 2013, a major theft occurred involving the Bitcoin—a primary player in the early days of the "cryptocurrency" movement. A Texas man was charged with using a Ponzi scheme to defraud investors of nearly $5,000,000 worth of this new currency. Setting a legal precedent, his case was ruled to be under the jurisdiction of the SEC because Bitcoins could also be exchanged for conventional currencies. Stored on a host of computer networks throughout the world, Bitcoins exist only in digital form and are nearly untraceable. A crime like this wouldn't have been possible just a few years ago, and although crime has existed for millennia, the types of crime (and the methods used to prevent and punish it) will look astonishingly different in the near future.

To help us better understand what crime could look like in the next decade, let's observe two young brothers, Rick and Allen, who grew up the poorest of their neighbors in a long-neglected and decaying part of town. Although their living quarters often changed, the presence of crime was a constant. Despite both growing up in the same difficult environment, the two brothers choose different paths for their lives. Rick was first caught pick-pocketing when he was twelve-years-old. His older brother Allen, on the other hand, decided at an early age he was going to become a police officer. Let's follow them into the early 2020s to see how upcoming changes in both crime and law enforcement shaped their lives.

FUTURE SCENARIO

One cold winter night, the boys' mother left the house to "find some cigarettes" and never came back. Rick was just four-teen and Allen sixteen. Rick was placed in a foster home but ran away soon after and supported himself by shoplifting. He was quite good at it and sold his stolen items mostly for "old cash" (not the more easily traceable polymer cash that was beginning to be used in the United States and Canada). This continued for months until one day, as Rick was eyeing an expensive new ultra-high resolution holographic scanner and planning how he was going to steal it, he was startled by a loud, almost imperceptibly digitized voice calling out "security alert!" Rick waited for a few minutes, and not seeing anyone approaching, grabbed the scanner. Just as he reached the door, he was apprehended by a member of store security and a local police officer who had recently been assigned to that particular store due to the recent rash of shoplifting incidents there. Rick was surprised to find out that a complex new security system had identified his body and eye movements were highly indicative of someone about to steal something. The "predictive" security alert was not only warning him not to steal, it was also alerting law enforcement.

Shortly after his arrest, Rick was interrogated in a room that looked to be completely empty save a small table and an odd-looking chair. From a speaker he couldn't see, he was asked a series of questions. To Rick it seemed as though the person asking the questions could read his mind. Within a few minutes, he confessed he was planning on stealing the scanner and that he had been shoplifting for months.

What Rick didn't realize was that there was no person on the other side asking questions and 'reading his mind'. An advanced interrogation system was being tested in that police department, and it had proven to be startlingly effective. The system used complex algorithms to process data from a variety of biological sensors and adapted its questions based on the physiological response of the person being interrogated. After a little fine-tuning, it quickly became the most effective lie detector ever developed.

With his full confession, Rick was easily convicted. Because he was a minor, and the judge was wary of the ethical implications of using confessions secured using this new technology, Rick was given a lenient sentence of three months in juvenile detention. This experience was enough for him to swear that he would never physically steal anything again. Rick knew he had to find a new way to support himself.

Always a quick study with computer systems, Rick decided to take the next few months to develop a new password hacking software that could steal credit card information and gain full access to social network profiles. He could then sell this software to buyers all over the world and take payments in nearly untraceable cryptocurrency. After years of warnings and pleading from companies to use biometric authentication (such as facial recognition or fingerprint scanning) instead of the now not-so-secure passwords, most people had recognized the risk and stopped using them almost completely. (There were, however, still those that thought a password such as their dog's name plus their house number was somehow more secure than biometrics for protecting their online bank account.) It would usually take Rick less than fifteen seconds to crack these "secure" passwords by using his new software to execute a program that aggregated and data-mined all relevant public and social network profiles as well as any updates they had posted or viewed privately. Most criminals found using this type of software much more effective than creating complicated algorithms to "blind crack" a password without using social network activity and other information available online.

Interestingly, police were now using similar technology to predict criminal activity and involvement. By analyzing a person's social networks, their web searches, and previous location data, the police could determine (with reasonable accuracy) the types of crimes a person was soon to be involved in. They hadn't used the new data harvesting technology to arrest anyone yet because, like in so many other areas, legislation was quickly falling behind the rapid advancements in technology. Rick knew though that he only had a few years left before financial companies and social networks would only accept a biometric login and he intended to make the most of those few remaining years.

By the time Rick was nineteen his prediction about password restrictions came true. Major companies were no longer allowing password-based account security and his previous method of generating income was now obsolete. Since he was anticipating this, he had spent a great deal of time attempting to create an expensive program that could mimic biometric logins. Unfortunately for him, such logins couldn't be 'guessed' and were extremely difficult to fake. In fact, he thought attempting to hack them was more likely than anything else to get him arrested again, so he gave up trying.

At about this same time, Rick was contacted by an anonymous person asking if he could write a program that would change where a company sent a large shipment of valuable Upsalite 3D printing cartridges. He had never thought of this criminal opportunity before, but after a few weeks he had the first version of his software virus worked out. To test it, he had a large pallet of dog food delivered to an upscale restaurant during the peak of their dinner rush. It worked—much to the confusion and embarrassment of the restaurant owners—and now Rick had a new business.

Soon, Rick was sending shipments of everything from advanced robotic prosthetics to electricity generating solar paint all over the world, and before the targeted company would even notice its loss, his program changed everything in their logistics system back to their original settings. The address where the shipments were sent would disappear from the records without a trace, and the numbers of items shipped were instantly modified so that they looked to be correct to whoever verified the shipments. But, since everything was usually automated now, an actual person rarely even looked at it.

Just before his final arrest, Rick began working on the most advanced version of his hack yet, a virus that was impossible to detect with current antivirus software. This new "zero-day virus" would also infect the machines of the intended receivers of each rerouted shipment. If he could change their records as well, it would take months for them to realize that they had been hacked. It was because of this new project that Rick was eventually caught.

Once again, it was the human component that failed. After spending a few fruitless hours online attempting to implant his malicious code into the automated shipping systems at a local warehouse, Rick became frustrated enough that he decided to physically break into the warehouse and transfer the software to the computers himself using the Near Field Communications (NFC) chip on his mobile device. After disabling the security system and locating the correct computer, Rick transferred his file in seconds.

What he didn't realize, though, was that police had stationed an observation drone with a high-powered camera over his house and had been watching his every move. As soon as he entered the warehouse, police seamlessly accessed a network of security cameras inside the warehouse and used them to witness the transfer of his virus to the company's computers. (Although still technically legal, both drone use for domestic surveillance and unauthorized access to private security camera networks by law enforcement were being bitterly fought against in various courthouses throughout the nation by citizens and groups concerned with privacy rights and ever-increasing government intrusion into their lives.) After Rick reset the building security system to cover up that he had been there, he turned around and was greeted by three police officers who arrested him. He was angry with himself because he had broken his only rule and had physically committed a crime! To Rick's relief, his brother Allen was not the one to make the arrest. The last time he checked, Allen was a street cop in a different part of the city.

Even though they had similar beginnings, Allen's life took a completely different course. Since he was sixteen when his mother left, Allen was able to enroll in a new government military program for at-risk youth. He knew it could give him a head start on the training he needed for a career in law enforcement. After he finished school, he completed two years in the National Guard and was able to secure a position as a policeman in his old hometown.

With robotics and automation now replacing many positions in factories and eliminating routine jobs, many people were now out of work. Because of this, while the number of cases of many types of crime (such as shoplifting) had dropped due to the advances in technology, street crime had been steadily increasing over the last half decade. Since such crimes were usually based on opportunistic criminals taking advantage of others in unplanned situations, officers found it difficult to accurately predict when and how these crimes would happen and that made them harder to prevent.

Even though he had a background in military intelligence, Allen asked to begin his law enforcement career as a street cop because he loved the new technology being employed. For example, as he walked down the street, a facial scanner silently alerted him if any known wanted person was nearby. A veteran policeman told Allen that these new scanners weren't like the first versions to see widespread use at the beginning of the decade. Those older models needed to be within two to five feet of the person to have a clear view of their face. The newest version now used a set of technologies that could be used to 'see' through facial hair, sunglasses, and even a full ski mask. Criminals quickly realized elaborate disguises were now of little use, and just made them look suspicious.

The new devices were also lighter, and no longer needed to be attached to a smartphone. He was also issued the latest model of the 'Bodyguard' electronic control device, which was a forearm-length glove that incorporated a stun gun, video camera, and shield plate used to deflect attacks, as well as features useful in helping law enforcement officers control their own sometimes aggressive tendencies. These tools made Allen's job as a police officer easier, and he was well aware of how much technology was changing law enforcement.

After a few years spent advancing in his first position with the department, Allen's enthusiasm and natural ability were recognized and he was promoted to the narcotics unit. Drugs that could be naturally grown, such as marijuana and mushrooms, were now legal (or at least decriminalized) in the majority of states, and most people had stopped using heavier drugs such as heroin and methamphetamines due to improved treatment technologies and safer fully synthetic alternatives. Allen was therefore tasked with scaling the entire department down to one unit that would focus on those few users still addicted to older drugs and who were unwilling or unable to get treatment at one of the new treatment facilities. Consolidating units and letting many of the drug enforcement officers go was difficult. After dedicating their entire careers to an unwinnable battle to stop drug use, the rapid changes in technology left many officers experts in a disappearing field.

After successfully realigning and consolidating his city's drug enforcement department, Allen was promoted to a new unit working as the chief cybercrimes investigator. Shortly after accepting this role, he realized he needed to address the substantial increase in the number of Internet-based crimes being committed against large manufacturing and shipping companies and the rapid growth of the "New Mafia" in his city.

Manufacturing and shipping companies, many of whom were still using outdated and easily accessible computers, found themselves the victims of relentless hacker intrusions. These cybercriminals gained access into the company's computers, repurposed the factory robots to assemble different products, and changed shipping addresses. The changes were often not recognized because of the widespread use of automated systems and the fact that the hackers only made small batches of their products and packaged them along with the company's intended product. In fact, law enforcement didn't discover that the manufacturing robots at one company were being repurposed until one day boxes full of bomb detonators were delivered by an autonomous delivery vehicle to a repair shop expecting car parts. Apparently, the hacker forgot to restore the robot's initial job instructions after fulfilling his last order of detonators.

In addition to this growing concern, another new category of crime was taking hold. The formation of a group called the "New Mafia" had begun in the city and, as of yet, local law enforcement was ill-equipped to deal with it. Hundreds of smart-device-equipped youth were now committing major coordinated crimes without even knowing each other. To earn money, they could add their mobile ID to a database controlled by a central hacking group. They paid a small fee to the group to be alerted to events such as flash mob style mass robberies at locations and times where there was sure to be a large gathering of wealthy individuals, such as a political fundraising dinner. Since only the participants knew when and where, and usually only at the last minute, these wide-scale attacks were nearly impossible to stop. The groups in control could also extort local businesses by threatening concentrated vandalism and theft to non-payers.

Shortly after Rick's arrest and conviction, Allen visited his brother in prison and was able to convince him that no matter what new type of crime he could dream up, with the new technology available to law enforcement—and with so much of the law enforcement budget now freed up to be used on stopping serious crime because of recent changes in drug laws—he would eventually get caught.

Finally, Rick realized that being a career criminal wasn't what he wanted to do with his life. Maybe he could even get a job in the police department's new hacker prevention division, where other ex-cons were being employed to help the police and private companies identify and fix security weaknesses as well as develop new methods to predict and prevent the growth of new crime. It was, at least, a profession where all of his years of being a cutting-edge criminal could actually help him be successful.

— BONUS QUESTIONS —

Violent crime rates in the United States have been dropping for years now. Do you think they will continue to drop? Will there ever be no crime?

Do you believe continued advances in neuroscience might help create a perfectly accurate lie detector?

Is it within the realm of possibility that data analytics could get so advanced that a person—a 'pre-criminal'—could be arrested for a crime they are _about_ to commit? Would this be ethical?

Will advancements in technology make things easier for criminals because they can commit crimes remotely over the Internet, or will it make it more difficult for them because law enforcement will also be using new technology?

What do you think will be the biggest crime-related problems in 2020?

Do you think it's possible to create an encryption that can't be hacked, or will criminals always be able to keep up with any advancement in security technology?

Do you think we will ever become a cashless society? If so, when do you think this could happen? Will this reduce crime?

There are currently tens of thousands of drones being flown in US airspace, with some being used by various law enforcement agencies to monitor American citizens. How will the extensive of use of drones domestically affect your businesses or your daily life? Are you in support of law enforcement agencies being allowed to use drones in the United States?

Do you think it's necessary for governments to monitor all of the online activity and phone calls of its citizens to keep them safe? How much privacy are you willing to compromise for the increased security this surveillance might potentially provide?

10

THE FUTURE OF BANKING: CUSTOMERS POCKET THE CHANGE

By the end of 2013, peer-to-peer lending services had issued $2.4 billion in loans, and it's estimated that in 2014 the amount lent will more than double to $5 billion. In the spring of the same year, Canada's Royal Bank hired IBM's Watson supercomputer as an engagement advisor to perform customer service; and DBS, a Singapore-based bank, revealed it would be using Watson to provide investing assistance to higher-end clients.

In late summer, Apple unveiled "Apple Pay" and announced it was teaming up with Target, McDonald's and three major credit card companies to allow consumers to make mobile payments via their smartphones and wearable devices. And then in the fall, PayPal and Dell both announced that they would begin accepting the digital cryptocurrency Bitcoin as a form of payment.

All of the aforementioned technological advances are in their early stages and will likely grow more influential by the end of the decade. The trends also suggest sweeping change for the banking and financial services industry in the coming years. As Bill Gates once famously said, "Banking will remain necessary in the future, banks may not."

The following scenario is a conversation between Stella, a 40-year old millennial and Brad, her 60-year-old wealth advisor, and takes place in the year 2020. Their discussion hints at many of the changes the financial services industry will need to make if it wishes to remain relevant in the future.

FUTURE SCENARIO

After reading the print edition of the *Wall Street Journal*, Brad sat down behind his desk and voice activated his desktop display. He asked to see the latest customer based alerts and the first item to appear was a report produced by his bank's "supercomputer" (it was actually a network of high-end machines located in data centers around the country and working cooperatively). Based upon structured and unstructured data culled from social media sites, credit cards and other public records, the supercomputer estimated a 67 percent probability that Stella, a client of Brad's for the past 15 years, was in the market for a small business loan.

Also in the report was information that Stella's husband, Mark, had been laid off as a lab diagnostic technician due to the continued automation of the health care industry. Brad wasn't expecting that, and could see how it might affect Stella's current financial decision process.

The computer advised Brad to contact her as soon as possible. It then checked with Stella's personal assistant device and asked, "Brad, she appears to be available for a video chat now. Would you like me to see if she's willing to have a brief conversation with you?"

"Yes. Thanks," replied Brad, forgetting for the moment that he was speaking with a machine.

Moments later he was connected to Stella via a secure video link. After exchanging personal greetings and engaging in some small talk in which Brad asked about Stella's father—who had introduced the two shortly after Stella had graduated from college—the pair got down to business.

"I was just calling to check in on you. I wanted to see if there was anything regarding your banking or investment needs that I might help you with. Also, if you have time, I wanted to review your investment portfolio," asked Brad.

"I'm glad you called. I've been meaning to call you, actually," Stella said. "This is a little awkward, Brad, especially because I appreciate how much you've done for Mark and I these past few years, but I've been thinking about taking control of my own financial situation."

Never one to over-react, Brad calmly replied, "What's the issue? I value our relationship and would obviously like to see it continue. If I haven't been serving you well, I'd welcome the opportunity to make it right."

"Oh, it's not your service, Brad. You've been great. Your investment advice has been good and when we needed to refinance our home last year your bank's "one-click" e-mortgage was fast and convenient, and the interest rate was the lowest we could find. It's just that I'm having a hard time justifying your annual fees—especially now that my smartphone does things like anticipate my impulse purchases and encourage me to save, instead of spend."

"I see."

"But that's not all. My husband lost his job and we think now might be the best time to move forward with a business idea that we've been developing so we're in the market for a business loan. We're considering using CrowdSeed—the new peer-to-peer lending platform that we've seen offering other entrepreneurs competitive rates."

"I'm sorry to hear about Mark's job, but I'm glad that you're thinking about starting a business," replied Brad, knowing from his bank's supercomputer analysis that this was a distinct possibility. "I think we might be able to offer an attractive rate. What kind of business are the two of you considering?"

Stella provided a brief explanation of her husband's idea of manufacturing a new nano-fabric capable of filtering out water-borne diseases and marketing it to people in Africa and Asia who had a low-income and couldn't afford the more expensive water purifiers now being sold there.

In an explanation of why she thought her and her husband would be able to secure the crowdsourced funds, she went on to say, "Over a billion people still lack access to a safe water supply. As mobile devices and high-speed Internet access have taken root across the developing world there are now hundreds of millions of people capable of making micro-payments with secure digital currencies on their phones. We believe we can still make a fair profit if we charge $3 per square foot of fabric. This won't make us wealthy, but if we can make a decent living and help make the world a better place in the process, that's all we really need."

"That's exciting, Stella. It sounds promising. What kind of rate do you think you can get on CrowdSeed?"

"Well because Mark lost his job our risk profile has increased, so we're looking at a rate of about 8 percent. But Facebook is offering us a rate of 7.5 percent."

"Stella," replied Brad in a lecturing tone, "I'll warn you again—as I did when we last spoke—Facebook and other non-traditional lenders such as Amazon, Google and Wal-Mart might be able to offer you attractive rates but that's because they are using your personal data in other ways to make money off of you."

Brad added, "Now, my bank also collects data—and, of course, we too are in the business of making money—but our long-term goal is not to sell you more stuff but rather to help you achieve your long-term financial goals."

"I know," said Stella. "But money is money and if we can save $50 or $100 per month on our loan payments, what's not to like? Plus my smart devices are doing a great job of protecting me from the offers that those retailers and social media companies are always sending me."

"I tell you what. Let me have our analysts and software look over your profile and crunch some numbers and I'll get back to you in a few minutes. While we're waiting perhaps we can go over your portfolio."

Brad's computer picked up on the request for loan information, researching available interest rates for Stella. In a lighter tone, Brad then added, "In the process I'll also try to convince you why it's in your best interest to stay with our banking and wealth advisory services."

"It's the least I can do," replied Stella. Almost apologetically, she added, "I want you to know that it is nothing personal. With the change in Mark's employment status, and all of these new tools and options, I'm just watching every dollar we spend more closely."

"I understand and that's exactly what you should be doing. But let me begin by reminding you that, on average, our bank has reduced fees by 50 percent since 2015. And during this period, we have continued to serve our community quite well. In fact, over the past four years we have added an estimated half million people who were previously considered poor risks or "unbankable".

"I know and I appreciate what you've done by helping so many people save money, buy their first homes and start small businesses. It's just that the fees and extra charges are still more than I'd like to pay. For instance, I know that you and the other bankers are still working in a luxury downtown offices instead of virtual offices and I have a hard time paying for what I consider to be your bank's unnecessary overhead."

"That's a fair point," replied Brad, "but I'd remind you that we have slashed the number of branch offices by 70 percent since 2016. We still keep a few offices because we happen to believe that while video calls such as the one you and I are on now are great, there is still tremendous value in having face-to-face meetings with our clients and with the bank's employees working together in the same building."

"In fact, next Tuesday we're bringing in a world-renowned neuro-economist to our downtown office to share with our clients proven strategies to help them and their adult children save more. If you'd like, I'd be happy to send you and Mark an invitation. If you can't make it, you can also stream it live or watch it later when it's convenient for you."

"That sounds interesting. Let me check with him to see if he's available."

"Another reason our fees can't go much lower," continued Brad, "is because our overhead provides real value. With our new authentication methods that use iris, voice and vein identification, we have eliminated the need for passwords with any of our services. Our computing and artificial intelligence systems are also state of the art and we've hired an elite team of data scientists. Together, they have not only reduced client losses by 40 percent by better identifying and preventing fraud, but we are one of only a handful of firms that have beat the S&P benchmark over the past five years. So I'd argue that while you can find your own "artificial advisor" software programs to help you with your banking and investment needs, they won't be anywhere near as sophisticated as ours or have as much access to all of the current global market data. The money we make you more than covers the fees you pay." Brad could see Stella nodding her head in agreement.

"Lastly, I'll acknowledge that you can lower your business transaction costs by relying more on digital currencies but I'd simply remind you that in spite of some impressive advances, digital currencies are still volatile, prone to hacking and capable of quickly losing value. You use and invest in such currencies at your own risk."

Stella again nodded her head, replied, "That's fair," before adding, "I'm beginning to see your point. Is there anything else that I might not be considering that could help convince me to stay with you and the bank?"

"Well, let's see... I'd also remind you that as someone you've known and worked with for more than 15 years I'm sincerely interested in your financial well-being, not just in chasing commissions and management fees. For example, remember a few years ago, when you and Mark were considering financing a second car? Who was it that advised you that you could eliminate over $6000 a year in car payments, fuel and insurance by foregoing the purchase of an automobile and using a car-sharing service instead?"

"That's a good point, Brad. Thanks for reminding me. I've always appreciated the personal attention and interest you've given us and I have to admit that not every banker would put their client's financial interests before their own."

"That's not exactly a ringing endorsement of my profession," said Brad laughing. "But, seriously, I will end by offering you some compelling visual evidence that your portfolio has beaten the market eight of the past ten years." Using software that allowed Brad to project information onto to Stella's video display, he showed her a series of charts and graphs that documented how her investments had outperformed the general market by more than 3 percent, which netted her almost $75,000 in additional gains.

"Wow."

"Wow, is right," said Brad. "I'd say that those returns more than cover my fees. In fact, I'm confident I can continue to help you grow your money."

"I'm all ears," said Stella.

Continuing, Brad said, "Based on our analysis, you might be surprised at my next recommendation for your retirement portfolio. I'm going to suggest that you and Mark lower your exposure to the utility sector—which we believe is poised to significantly under-perform the market in the coming years due to continued advancement in renewable energy sources and micro-grid technologies, and reinvest that money in a peer-to-peer lending fund. The latter isn't going to make you rich but our system estimates it'll return six percent over the coming twelve months. That beats keeping your extra money in cash and watching inflation nibble away at it."

"You mean to tell me that you want to invest in some of the very companies that my husband and I are considering for a loan?"

"Yep," said Brad. "I hate to admit it but some of those peer-to-peer companies are doing a great job of vetting unconventional loan applicants and they are filling a need that traditional banks still aren't doing a good job of covering."

Again, Stella shook her head. Impressed at how quick Brad was to identify and adapt to new opportunities.

"Now let's get back to your loan," said Brad. "Our big electronic brain has crunched the numbers and I'm sorry to report that we can't match the rate you can get on CrowdSeed."

Stella was a little surprised. "Can I ask why?"

"Sure," said Brad. "Since you've been candid with me, I'll be candid with you. Our software has identified three other companies that are already in more advanced stages of developing similar technologies, and our analysts don't calculate your ability to compete very favorably."

"But now let me say this. I know you and Mark, and one of the reasons why my bank is still in existence is because we believe in our community. I'd encourage the two of you to do more due diligence on your business plan and if you do take the CrowdSeed loan, and if your company needs additional capital to grow, my bank would love to grow with you. I'm confident that in time you will have more data to convince our computers, and we'll be able to beat the rate you're getting from the peer-lending services. Also, I know how socially conscious you and Mark are, so I think we should schedule a time to all get together and discuss some of the new ways you can begin to create a lasting legacy. We have some incredible options for doing the most amount of good in the world with what you have, such as leveraging the power of your donations using micro-loan platforms and through creating online matching programs for causes you care about. I know that helping people around the world is much more important to you two than possibly having your name on a building someday. I can help you find the best ways to do that, in addition to the other services you already enjoy. Sound fair?"

Stella gently nodded, and said, "That's fair. In the meantime, I'll keep my money with you but you'll have to continue convincing me of the value you're providing."

"Of course. Good luck with your new business and hopefully I'll see you Tuesday at the presentation."

— BONUS QUESTIONS —

Would you ever consider taking out a loan from a peer-to-peer lending platform? Would you ever consider investing in such a platform?

Do you believe that by 2020 artificial intelligence will be capable of providing you better financial advice than a financial service professional?

If mobile payments and digital crypto-currencies are proven to be safe, effective and reliable, can you envision accepting them as a form of payment? How might such currencies allow unconventional business to succeed?

How frequently do you visit a physical bank or credit union? Do you believe your behavior will change in the coming years?

How might technology continue to change the consumption and purchasing habits of people in the future? For example, if car-sharing or boat-sharing services continue to become more popular, how do you think it would impact the loan and banking system?

How might non-traditional or "shadow banking" companies such as Google, Apple, Wal-Mart, Facebook and Amazon transform the financial services industry?

Does "Big Data" represent a threat or an opportunity to the banking industry? What about an individual's rights to keep their personal information secure?

How do all of these possibilities, and the possibility of living to well over 100 due to rapid advancements in health care, affect your ideas about saving and retirement?

11

FROM THE BOARDROOM TO THE BEDROOM AND EVERYWHERE IN BETWEEN: THE FUTURE OF ROBOTICS

Introduced in the fall of 2012, Baxter–a new generation of industrial robot–is changing our perceptions of what a factory robot can be. Once incredibly expensive, dangerous, and difficult to control and manage, industrial robots are entering a new era with the introduction of Baxter. The robot doesn't need a safety cage because it's aware of nearby human workers and obstacles, it doesn't require any programming–you simply show it what to do–and best of all it starts at around $25,000. And, in the fall of 2013, Baxter's manufacturer released a free software update that significantly improved its overall performance. This single software update may seem insignificant but it points towards a future where more robots that, like Baxter, run on the open-source software systems, can be quickly and inexpensively updated–similar to how we update our smartphones and tablets today.

To appreciate robotics' extraordinary advances by the end of this decade, let's catch up with Gerhardt, who was recently promoted to senior vice president of Robotic Business Development at a large multinational corporation in Berlin, Germany. After spending his first decade-and-a-half at the company in the field of robotics, he is the perfect fit for the position.

FUTURE SCENARIO

Gerhardt came to the attention of his employer after leading the University of Bielefeld to the Robocup championship where his team of nimble robots crushed the team from Singapore Polytechnic. His first job with the company was helping install the company's prototype automated robotic warehouse. Less than two years later, Gerhardt was promoted to oversee the entire operation.

After it was calculated that the warehouse robots had saved the company millions of euros by reducing labor costs, speeding up delivery time and reducing energy costs (which were achieved because robots don't require as much space to move about, and because they can work without lights and in colder temperatures), Gerhardt was placed in charge of the company's worldwide transition to robotic warehouse systems. In this capacity, he was recognized by company executives as just the expert in implementing robotic systems they needed to spearhead new robotic endeavors throughout the organization. This was as much for the political acumen Gerhardt demonstrated in easing tensions with unions and the media over concerns that robots were threatening traditional trade jobs as it was for his expertise in robotics.

In an effort to give him more exposure to how the company was planning on using robotics, Gerhardt was cross-transferred to a major airfreight client where he worked on integrating self-driving forklifts and trucks into the company's global supply chain. His particular focus was improving self-driving robots' safety and reliability, and he left the project only after his robots performed without an accident for six months.

Gerhardt followed this work with a temporary assignment at the Fraunhofer Institute, Europe's largest application-oriented research organization, where he worked in the field of 'swarm' robotics and studied how large numbers of robots could work in coordination to achieve larger goals. In Gerhardt's case, he specialized in developing an 'ant army' of micro-robots that could work together efficiently in search-and-rescue operations. His work was later credited with rescuing scores of people in Turkey after an earthquake leveled an apartment building.

Noting how rescue workers bonded on an emotional level with their robotic search-and-rescue companions, Gerhardt took what many of his peers considered a risky career move and agreed to help the company expand into the educational marketplace by creating robots that appeared more humanlike. After suffering a series of setbacks, Gerhardt's decision to change positions was ultimately vindicated when some of his robots were more successful in tutoring children with special needs than previous attempts had been. It was a source of special pride for Gerhardt that children with autism often responded better to lessons given by his robots than they did with their human teachers, and that his robots helped behavioral scientists develop effective treatments to help them better manage the disorder.

It was Gerhardt's unique combination of experience with traditional manufacturing robots as well as personal service robots that helped him secure his next position, serving as the company's first-ever Director of Robotic Resources. In this newly created position—which generated some friction within the organization when he was given responsibilities equal to those of the director of human resources—Gerhardt was charged with overseeing the corporation's entire fleet of robots, including everything from those that staffed the warehouses, cleaned the hallways, and provided security in the parking lots, to the growing number of personal telepresence robots which were used by company employees to attend meetings remotely. The latter robots alone were estimated to have saved the company $37 million in travel costs and reduced its carbon footprint by eighty-four million tons.

The job, however, had its moments. Gerhardt's greatest challenge came when he was tasked with overseeing the company's crisis management response team in the wake of a fatal accident in which an automated warehouse robotic system killed one employee and damaged millions of euros' worth of inventory. Although human error was later found to be a major contributing factor to the fatality, many warehouse workers were quick to blame the robotic system. It was eventually determined that the workers were hoping the accident would cause management to reconsider the move to greater automation, and thus ensure their job security—at least temporarily.

After serving in this position for three years, Gerhardt was tapped to lead the corporation's expansion into developing new robots for the military, educational, health care, and aging services markets under the company's new Developing Robotics division. As part of his responsibilities, he regularly visited the company's North American research and development facility located a few miles outside of Cleveland, Ohio.

On this particular day, Gerhardt's first stop was the educational lab where company researchers and roboticists were developing a new generation of robots designed to serve as classroom assistants. Fueled by their extraordinary success in assisting children with special needs, the company was keen on reaching a wider audience. Gerhardt was also eager to expand this business because he knew the timing was right. Since the beginning of the decade, the robotics toy market had grown at a CAGR (compounded annual growth rate) of 80 percent and now more than half of all children in North America, East Asia, and Europe owned at least one robot. In short, even though parents might not have yet been ready to embrace robotic instructors, Gerhardt was confident their children were.

Gerhardt watched as one experimental robot, capable of displaying 156 unique humanlike expressions, monitored a classroom of rambunctious kindergartners. Using its onboard cameras and sophisticated facial recognition technology, the robot was able to detect that a particular child was having a difficult time understanding the rules of the game she wanted to play. At a gentle pace and careful to avoid bumping into the other children who were running around it, the robot addressed the girl by her first name and asked, "Can I answer any questions for you?"

Thinking nothing unusual of a robot speaking to her, the girl looked into its face—which had intentionally been designed to look friendly, but not like a human—and responded, "Yes. I don't understand the game."

"Have you read the rules?" asked the robot. The student nodded affirmatively. "Do you understand all of the words?" The girl sheepishly replied that she did. Sensing the hesitation in her voice, the robot projected the instructions on the wall. It had pulled the instructions from a radio-frequency identification (RFID) tag embedded in the game's box. It then asked if there were any words she didn't understand. The girl pointed to the words 'diagonal' and 'reverse'. The robot provided formal definitions and then focused its projector on the game board and demonstrated the rules in action.

"Oh, that's easy," she replied in a satisfied tone.

A few moments later, the robot detected the student was again frustrated. This time, however, upon hearing a tone that it recognized as confrontational, the robot alerted a teacher in another room and transmitted a live video stream to the instructor of what was happening; two students were fighting over the game. The teacher rushed to the scene and peacefully resolved the issue without having to threaten to ask the robot what (or who) caused the problem. Gerhardt was pleased with the demonstration. It was the company's stated goal not to use robots to replace teachers but to help them better interact and engage with students at those points when personalized instruction was essential. (Although, to him it seemed all but inevitable that some human teachers would eventually be replaced. First, out of necessity in areas where there weren't enough teachers, but eventually because robots with advanced human interaction abilities could do a much a better job of educating.)

Following a brief video conference with officials of Fédération Internationale de Football Association (FIFA), he discussed how his company's miniature butterfly-like robots could be used to discreetly monitor the crowds at the 2022 World Cup soccer games in Qatar (and thus prevent any repeats of the ugly hooligan incidents that had marred the 2018 games in Russia). Next, Gerhardt strolled to the second floor of the research and development lab and peeked in on the company's latest attempts to develop robots that were better able to assist the world's growing number of senior citizens.

At Gerhardt's urging, the company had made a strategic decision to supplement its traditional home-aide robotic business with the creation and development of exoskeletons, or wearable robotics. Recent advances in flexible electronics and nanomaterials made the devices extremely lightweight and much less obvious and restrictive than previous models. The technology also had the added benefit of giving seniors what they really wanted–independence. While some seniors enjoyed using brain-neural devices to control external robots to perform household chores such as getting a cup of coffee or washing laundry, the vast majority still preferred doing these things themselves.

This is not to say that a market didn't exist for wearable robots. In fact, Gerhardt was convinced that because of accelerating advances in biotechnology, genomics, and regenerative medicine, the fastest growing demographic segment for robotics' would be 'super' seniors–or those people over 100 years of age. And since exoskeletons were currently inappropriate for this demographic segment due to their cost, complexity, and weight, Gerhardt felt the company should focus its efforts on alternative robotic solutions for them.

Unlike their younger counterparts, this segment of the market required robotics that addressed the unique needs that resulted from aging. The most serious of which was loneliness, and Gerhardt was well versed in the research documenting how effective pets were in minimizing depression. (To this end, he personally took the lead in the effort to develop a series of new non-allergenic robotic pets that, in addition to serving as companions, could also serve as health monitors and send alerts to family members or health care providers if their master's condition was suggestive of a more serious problem.)

The features made robotic pets a popular gift for children to give their aging parents, but Gerhardt was even more optimistic that within the year the federal governments of Japan, Germany, and the United States would begin covering the cost of robots for those patients who could demonstrate the device's primary purpose was health care related.

After peering in on the status of a new surgical robotic device to assist in treating brain aneurysms, Gerhardt's final visit of the day took him to the company's 'skunk lab' where researchers were working on the company's most controversial project— adult entertainment robots. Setting aside his own personal and moral objections to these robots, Gerhardt was aware history had amply demonstrated that the industry most likely to embrace new technology—be it the video cassette tape or the Internet—was the adult entertainment industry. In Gerhardt's mind it was inevitable that robotics would follow suit. Indeed, his company was already behind the curve in this regard. One of his competitors already had on the market a life-sized robot capable of giving a ninety-minute massage.

Gerhardt was informed by a fellow roboticist in the lab that the touch and feel of its hands were indistinguishable from the hands of a real person. It didn't surprise him, but he did wonder how he was going to inform his younger brother, who was a professional massage therapist, of this latest development. He then contemplated how far the entire field of robotics had progressed since he graduated from college and he could only laugh. It was one thing to construct a robot to play a game by kicking a soccer ball, it was altogether something different to construct a robot that could engage in the most intimate of human activities.

— BONUS QUESTIONS —

Lately, numerous robots have been created that can do jobs once thought to be only possible for a human. Do you think it will ever be possible for a robot to do your job? If not, what aspects of your job do you think will always require a human?

Think about how much we already rely on machines. What would happen if those machines were no longer available, or even temporarily offline? What risk does handing a growing number of our decisions off to automation pose?

In March 2012 the state of Nevada made it legal for self-driven robotic cars to operate. Since then Florida, California, Michigan, and the District of Columbia have followed suit. Nearly all major car manufacturers are currently working on developing self-driving cars and many have stated that they will have consumer models available before the end of the decade. Would you like to be chauffeured around in a self-driving car? What about an aging parent or relative using self-driving vehicles to reclaim some of their independence?

Would you ever consider purchasing a robotic assistant for yourself or your family? Would it need to have strength and size limitations before you would purchase it?

What jobs do you think robots (or automated machinery) will never be able to do?

In Japan, robots are already beginning to be used to care for the elderly. Would you trust a robot to take care of an elderly parent or relative?

Exoskeletons are now being sold to paraplegics, allowing them to stand and move in an upright position and the field of prosthetics has been making major advancements in the last few years. If you were to lose a limb, would you consider having it replaced with a robotic device?

Do you think that there will be a day when robots will be indistinguishable from humans?

12

ENGINES OF CHANGE: THE FUTURE OF SIMULATED INTELLIGENCE

For three days in February 2011, Watson, an IBM supercomputer battled the game show Jeopardy's top two all-time winners, Ken Jennings and Brad Rutter, in a nationally televised contest pitting man against machine. The machine won. In addition to highlighting the amazing processing speed of computers as well as the growing sophistication of algorithms, the contest yielded an intriguing but incomplete glance into the future of computer intelligence and how it can be used.

On his response to the final question, when it was clear he was going to lose, Jennings scribbled the words, "I, for one, welcome our new computer overlords," below his answer. Although the statement may have been intended to be comical, many people will, in fact, come to welcome the intelligent machines and personal devices of the future, because they will be able to do so much more than just access vast reams of digital content to answer obscure trivia questions. Intelligent machines will understand the precise context, location, and needs of an individual making a query, and scan vast databases of print, audio, and video to provide answers to nuanced questions. Indeed, they will even be able to anticipate future needs. In fact, intuitive software is currently being developed by companies around the world, including giants such as Google, Microsoft, and Facebook, that can do just that. Google Now can already determine places and events that are likely important to you and pro-actively make suggestions based on how well it 'knows' you. In early 2014, IBM announced a new billion dollar division to identify and create new uses for Watson and one innovative venture capital firm has already 'appointed' Watson to serve on its board of directors. The company has also opened an app challenge for developers to bring Watson to your smartphone or tablet.

Additionally, the long promised goal of creating true artificial intelligence is finally moving closer to reality as numerous well-funded startups and legacy companies continue to make breakthroughs, such as the achievement Facebook announced in March 2014. Its DeepFace software was able to match faces with 97.25% accuracy—performing on par with human testers. Certainly by the end of the decade even more impressive announcements regarding artificial intelligence will be made and the possibilities are both exciting and potentially concerning.

To better understand the abilities of the computers of tomorrow, let's take a look in on the family of Omar and Camille, two professionals living in the Washington, DC area. Omar serves as legal counsel to the chairwoman of the Senate Energy Committee, and his wife, Camille, a native of Lyon, France, is an architect specializing in using bio-mimicry in design. She works for a construction firm dedicated to building high security diplomatic buildings that also incorporate natural elements. Let's begin our visit on a typical morning as the family begins to prepare for their day.

FUTURE SCENARIO

Calibrated to a frequency only he can hear, Omar's alarm wakes him and he heads to the bathroom. After closing the door, an electronic display embedded in the bathroom mirror shows him a prioritized list of all news items and messages he has received since the previous evening. The list was created by his personal assistant, or PA, a complex software package that has progressively learned Omar's personal habits and preferences by monitoring his actions (including his purchases and social network posts) over the past five years. The program, which Omar named Rosie (after a robotic cartoon character from his youth), exists in the cloud and seamlessly transfers to whichever platform best serves Omar. It also knows what news items and messages he'll find most important, whom he is likely to respond to first (and those he routinely ignores) and when he is amenable to receiving a targeted advertisement. It can even identify and draw his attention to important details of people in his social network—such as birthdays, anniversaries, promotions, and other milestones.

The top item on Omar's list this morning is a story translated from a website dedicated to tracking cold fusion developments in India. Next on the list is a story from National Public Radio (NPR) covering the previous day's committee hearings that focused on the status of cold fusion research. This is followed by a series of links to videos of interviews with Democrats, Republicans, Centrists, independents, and industry representatives regarding yesterday's testimony.

Omar first selects the story from NPR because he can listen to it while he showers. Next, he selects the video clip of the chairwoman on a new political news network because he believes it is the least polarized media outlet and offers the most objective review of the hearing. Omar watches a clip of the interview on the display on his fog-free, digitally integrated mirror while shaving.

After dressing, Omar proceeds downstairs. His PA, Rosie, tells him the kitchen contains all of the ingredients necessary to make Camille's favorite breakfast, a piperade omelet and lyonnaise potatoes. It also informs him his wife has just woken up and he shouldn't start preparing her breakfast yet. Omar unfolds his flexible tablet and uses the free time to read a comprehensive sampling of translated stories from Brazilian, German, and Chinese news sources on yesterday's hearing.

While getting ready, Camille glances at a similar list of prioritized items her PA, whom she refers to as CC (which stands for cyber clone), has created. Camille, however, ignores the list and pulls up an old video lecture she asked CC to locate the evening before. Hand gesturing for the video to play, a clip from an old graduate school lecture by her favorite professor pops up on screen and he can be seen discussing the beauty and complexity of conch shells. CC interrupts the video with a message that there is a small window of time in which Camille can discuss the final design feature for the new Kurdistan embassy with her colleagues in Shanghai and Stockholm. Given the time zone differences, Camille knows it's rare that all of her coworkers are available at the same time and approves the request. It takes less than a minute for CC to coordinate with her colleagues' PAs and arrange a three-way conference call.

Camille shows her colleagues a snippet from her old professor's lecture and displays (via a secure intracompany portal) a three-dimensional model of a spiral staircase in the lobby of the embassy. Its structure is modeled on a conch seashell. "It's elegant, sturdy, and can be manufactured with 3D printed sustainable materials," says Camille. Her colleagues agree it's a perfect fit for the embassy.

It also happened to be the last major design component needed to finish the building plans. To celebrate the completion of the project, CC recommends sending a bouquet of stargazer lilies to her colleague in Shanghai and a bottle of Japanese sake to the one in Stockholm. Camille is confident they will both enjoy the gifts because CC, after scanning her colleagues' social network interactions, listed a series of gifts they would likely enjoy. The two items she chose had a confidence ranking of 97 percent and Camille had never had a bad experience with an item rated 95 percent or above. She then asks CC to recommend a French wine her old professor might enjoy. Almost before she finishes asking, CC has recommended a bottle of 2006 Chevalier-Montrachet. Camille approves the three gifts, confident the items will be shipped within the hour, and her bank account is correctly debited and her tax records are updated to reflect that the three purchases were legitimate business expenses.

The quick resolution of her work allows Camille to join her husband for a relaxing breakfast. She enjoys and appreciates that Omar always knows what to make for her, but is aware this is as much due to Rosie's databases as her husband's memory. Camille tells Omar she intends to modify their investment portfolio. Although investing is still subject to the complexities of the global marketplace, CC has greatly reduced the risk by searching a wide variety of informational sources, including trade publications, financial journals, and long-range weather forecasts. With the freshly gathered information, CC estimates there is 78 percent probability drought conditions in Russia and Australia will persist into next year. Based on the information, Camille tells her husband she would like to sell some stock and put a long-term option on wheat. Omar just shrugs. He's comfortable leaving the investment decisions to Camille—and CC.

By the time their portfolio has been reconfigured, Benton and Madison, Omar and Camille's two children, have joined them at the breakfast table. The ensuing conversation is remarkably stress-free because everyone's calendar is synchronized; Madison's PA has reminded her she needs to pack her clarinet for music class and her shin guards for soccer practice, while Benton's PA has noted he still needs to post the history project that is due today. Benton's PA has even sent a note to Omar, reminding him not to pack a peanut butter sandwich that day because Benton will be sitting at a lunch table with a classmate who has a peanut allergy.

The fluid and almost imperceptible schedule coordination allows the family to concentrate on planning their upcoming trip to New York City over the Thanksgiving holiday. Unfortunately, this activity is not as stress-free as the previous calm breakfast, since everyone's PA has pulled up a different personalized list of things to do. Camille's agenda is more focused on peer-based recommendations because it knows she will pay greater attention to the suggestions of her friends and acquaintances. Omar's list is the complete opposite and concentrates on the opinions of travel experts. The first problem arises when they begin comparing restaurants to visit while in Manhattan.

The situation escalates as Madison and Benton's PAs begin showing them New York City video suggestions of fun activities other children their ages have enjoyed while visiting the Big Apple. Madison's PA, for example, knows she is interested in theater, while her brother's PA pulls up hotels that will accommodate Harry, the family's beagle since it knows Benton prefers to bring the dog on vacation.

In a matter of minutes, most of the major issues are resolved as Rosie (the family's de facto mediator in such situations) is able to classify and prioritize all the issues. Rosie does this by laying out the information and decision points in a visual manner that allows each family member to better understand the various tradeoffs. Omar was most concerned with keeping the trip within the family budget and Rosie presented him with an infographic showing him that while the train was more expensive than flying, the time they would save by arriving directly at Penn Station would more than compensate for the higher cost of the train. Algorithmically identifying the perplexed look on his face, Rosie responded by saying, "Remember, time is money. The train will save your family an estimated total of four hours and thirty-two minutes."

Camille was able to prevail on most of her restaurant selections for dinner because Rosie reminded Omar that he didn't enjoy two of the past three restaurants the New York Times' top restaurant critic had selected. "I keep telling you," replied Camille in a smug tone, "the future of intelligent search is finding and listening to what the people you know and trust think... not the so-called experts."

The kids were less happy because Rosie recommended keeping Harry at home. The majority of pet-friendly hotel rooms in New York had already been reserved and the additional price the family would have had to pay would have been prohibitive. Rosie instead made a tentative reservation for Harry at Dog Heaven, a local kennel, because only two spots remained over the Thanksgiving holiday. Recognizing its current settings required his approval before paying for the transaction, Rosie prompted Omar to confirm the reservation. "The last spot was about to be taken," the PA responded as a matter of explaining why it had made the original decision without any prompting from Omar. To appease the children, Rosie recommended using the savings to purchase four tickets to Broadway's latest hit show, *Tron: Off the Grid*. It knew that both parents enjoyed the original 1982 movie and the kids loved the 2010 sequel.

With all the hard decisions for the day made before 8am, Omar and Camille got their kids on the bus early (because they were alerted it was arriving two minutes ahead of schedule) and then lamented what effect the advancements in simulated intelligence devices were having on their kids' minds. "I worry their PAs are doing all of their thinking for them, and that when they get older they won't be able to think for themselves," said Camille. Omar nodded in agreement.

Not recognizing the irony, the two then tried to use CC to book a two-week summer vacation in northern Vermont. To gain a competitive advantage in the commercial marketplace, a small, rustic resort had recently created an old-fashioned 'digital-free' retreat. The number of people wishing to escape the conveniences of modern technology had exceeded the resort owner's wildest expectations and openings were limited. Alas, because the resort didn't accept reservations from electronic personal assistants, Omar had to call the resort himself. After being placed on a five-minute hold, which seemed like an eternity, Omar nervously booked a reservation for his family.

— BONUS QUESTIONS —

Do you have a smartphone, tablet, or wearable device, such as a smart watch? Just a few years ago, most of us didn't. How much do you rely on your smart device in your everyday life?

If digital personal assistants such as Apple's Siri, Google Now, or Microsoft's Cortana become 1000-fold more powerful in the coming decade, what jobs and industries do you believe will be most impacted?

Do you think we will ever be able to fully interact with computers using only our minds?

If real time, accurate language translation software becomes possible by 2020, will new markets around the world open up for your business? Would it still be beneficial to learn a second or third language?

Do you think you can make better stock market investment decisions than sophisticated algorithms capable of processing millions of pieces of data in a single second? If so, why?

How does our educational system need to change in an environment where complex questions can be rapidly answered by machines?

What are the negative consequences of becoming overly reliant on artificial intelligence?

Do you think, as scores of science fiction works suggest, that artificial intelligence could one day pose a threat to humanity?

13

IN THE FUTURE, IT'S ALL A GAME:
THE FUTURE OF GAMING DYNAMICS

A restroom in a Japanese pub might be a curious place to catch a glimpse of the future, but if you look closely, it's there. Sega, the large Japanese entertainment company, installed four types of "Toylet" games designed to influence the users' behaviors. In one game "Graffiti Eraser", male patrons aim at a pressure sensor in the urinal with the goal of erasing the virtual graffiti on a flat-panel screen directly in front of them. The purpose is twofold. If the user is successful in the game, the restroom stays cleaner. Less obvious is the idea that the person participating in the game is motivated to pay closer attention to the advertisement as it is revealed from behind the virtual graffiti.

It's a crude method of changing a person's behavior, but the game points toward a growing trend: gaming dynamics or gamification—the intentional use of technology and incentives (mixed with a healthy dose of psychology) to influence human behavior in a specific manner and/or toward a desired objective.

Let's follow Todd, a man in his mid-twenties, through the course of a typical day to better understand the immense potential of gaming dynamics.

FUTURE SCENARIO

After waking up, Todd brushes his teeth with his Internet-connected toothbrush because he knows his dentist will reward his diligence by crediting his account one hundred points and that once he reaches five-thousand-points, he'll receive a 20 percent discount on future services. Todd continues to brush for a full two minutes because he also knows Proctor & Gamble is sponsoring a game to encourage good brushing habits. If he brushes twice a day for at least two minutes, Todd will receive a complimentary tube of Crest next time he visits any store that carries that brand.

While eating breakfast, Todd is sure to verify, via his Healthy Eating app, that he has limited his intake to less than 500 calories and eaten the equivalent of five servings of fruit. The information is fed into a Nike-sponsored game call "Lifelog" and it updates to show Todd he has pulled ahead in his quest to beat his old college roommate in their contest to see who can add the most years to their avatar. Todd is proud that since he began playing, he's added the equivalent of two full years of life expectancy to his avatar. By association, Todd also knows he is living a healthier life—which is exactly the lifestyle message Nike is hoping he'll associate with the game.

After breakfast, Todd debates whether to ride the bus or drive to work. His personal assistant on his smartphone convinces him that while riding the bus will garner him fifteen points which can be redeemed at year's end for a tax credit from the state of Massachusetts, he should instead opt for renting an automobile from a car-sharing service.

On the recommendation of his girlfriend Gina, Todd selects a fuel-cell hybrid vehicle because he knows Gina will receive five extra 'friend referral' points which she can apply toward her account. When a notification pops up on her smart device alerting her of Todd's rental, Gina is thrilled because she now has enough points for a free rental during her upcoming trip to the West Coast.

Upon getting into the car, Todd immediately looks at the dashboard and notices the previous driver was only able to get the virtual tree on the console to bloom half of its leaves. It is a sure sign the driver wasn't an experienced hyper-miler, a coveted status awarded only to those drivers capable of achieving more than 150 MPGe (miles per gallon gasoline equivalent). By accelerating carefully, maintaining an optimum speed and coasting to stops, Todd is able to get the entire virtual tree to bloom. In return for his mastery of the "Green Tree" game, the car-sharing service rewards him with a five percent discount, the equivalent of the amount of fuel he saved.

Based on his driving prowess and the city of Boston's new game, "Ride Share" which was designed to take cars off of the city streets by encouraging people to carpool with others in their broader social network, Todd is once again able to get to work ahead of schedule. His early arrival is logged by his employer who is aware he has arrived at work early the equivalent of one full week in the past year. In return for his diligence, Todd notices that the pink piggy bank icon on his foldable, flexible electronic tablet has just grown one percent, a signal his employer has made good on its promise to make an additional contribution to his individual retirement account in return for extra hours worked. (This program was later canceled by his employer, however, as many employees were gaming the system and simply coming in early and using the extra time to shop online, watch videos, and update their social networks. The only thing they weren't able to do was nap, a practice that had ended years ago, due to alertness sensors installed throughout the office.)

Moments later, Todd is startled when he hears additional money being dropped into his account. He looks at the accompanying text message and sees it is a notice from the federal government. Todd has just met the minimum annual savings requirement under the government's new trial game, "Your Choice, Your Retirement". In return for his frugality, Todd has received the equivalent of an additional two percent savings bonus from Uncle Sam. The game was instrumental in convincing younger voters to agree with the president's plan to reform the Social Security system in 2017.

Following lunch, Todd signs in to the latest version of "Foldit", an immersive 3D game that allows players to virtually fold proteins in an effort to cure diabetes. The game's popularity has skyrocketed since it was instrumental in turning Alzheimer's into a treatable condition in 2019. In an effort to assess the game's progress, Todd's employer, a DNA analysis company, has given him $10,000 in virtual currency, which he can wager on the date a cure for diabetes might be achieved. Todd's bet is then aggregated with those of his fellow employees. Company management reviews the results because it understands that aggregated, crowd-sourced predictions routinely beat the predictions of experts and it intends to use this predictive group intelligence to determine the best time to begin marketing their new genetic test for diabetes.

After work, Todd goes to his health club where he jumps into the virtual boxing ring to let off some of the stress of his job as a genetic health counselor and spars for seven rounds against an opponent from Vladivostok, Russia. Todd is about to quit when the sensors embedded in his Reebok workout shirt alert him that his old roommate went ten rounds earlier in the day and burned 750 calories. Not to be outdone, Todd matches his buddy's total and is notified shortly thereafter by his insurance company that he's within reach of meeting the standard necessary to receive a reduction on his health insurance premium under its "It Pays to Lose" game. Exhausted, Todd presses on and completes a full fifteen rounds. His reward is a fifty dollar savings off next month's insurance bill.

Wanting to celebrate the end of his great day, Todd uses a location-based app on his smart device to automatically send a message to any friends in the vicinity of his health club to see if they are up for grabbing a drink. As soon as he initiates the search, an ad for Dusty's Bar & Saloon pops up and notifies him that if four or more of his friends join him at the bar they will all receive Happy Hour prices for the entire evening. After they meet up, Todd's friends compare the deal with the others they have just received on their devices and decide it is the best deal. One friend, however, misses out on the deal, because she, like a growing number of people, is swearing off anything that employs gaming dynamics. (In her case, she soured on the concept after receiving a poor grade in her MBA program from a professor who based final grades on the number of experience points a student accumulated over the course of a semester.)

Once at the bar, Todd buys the first round because he knows by the flashing nacho icon on his smartwatch that he'll receive a free appetizer as a reward for spending seventy-five dollars at Dusty's this month. After he's polished off his first beer, Todd heads to the bathroom and is confronted with the latest version of the "Toylet" game, "Firefighter" where instead of graffiti, he finds a virtual fire to extinguish. He expertly hits the pressure sensors and puts out the fire, which rewards him with an ad containing a two-for-one coupon to be used on his next beer purchase.

Todd declines the e-coupon but forwards a game credit to his favorite charity, a nature conservation alliance, where it is re-deemed for a modest cash donation. Todd feels good about the donation but knows the real reason he opted against the extra beer was because he feared the extra calories might cause his old roommate to catch up with him in their "A Year in the Life" game as well as put in jeopardy the health insurance bonus he had just worked so hard to win earlier in the evening.

Tired and ready for bed, Todd geo-locates his girlfriend, Gina, who just happened to have rented a nearby car. She happily picks him up because she knows she'll get extra tax credit points from both the city and state governments and that she can spend a few minutes of quality time telling him about her day on the way to his house. After getting dropped off at his apartment, Todd goes to bed... but not before brushing his teeth.

— BONUS QUESTIONS —

By 2015, Gartner Research estimates that seventy percent of all Fortune 1000 companies will employ a chief gaming officer. Would your company benefit from a gaming officer?

To cultivate more loyal customers, how could gaming dynamics be employed by your company?

Could your industry use gaming dynamics to improve employee education and training? What about improving employee productivity and time-management?

If you were given a substantial discount on your insurance premium, would you allow your insurance company to have access to your personal monitoring device (e.g. FitBit, Jaw-Bone, Nike+, or FuelBand) so they could track activities such as you going to gym or eating at healthy restaurants?

Does a future of gaming elements being added to many everyday activities seem like a fun way to get special deals and earn discounts, or does it seem like just another invasion of privacy that's not worth a few discounts or more relevant product and service recommendations?

Do you think that eventually people will grow tired of so many aspects of their lives being gamified that there begins to be a backlash against it?